Contents

Introduction to this *Assessment Kit*

I have to say that, speaking from the 'chalk-face', assessment is always a bit of a nightmare! With around thirty children in the class, and an ever-increasing pressure on producing yet more documentation and evidence, the whole thing can, if we are not careful, simply add to the stress levels of both teachers and children. But assessment is of course essential, so let's first agree two things about productive assessment:

- We should remember that we do not feed a child by weighing them. An assessment, no matter how good, is not the child. It should neither constrain our expectations nor limit our endeavours.
- Assessments of any kind are always provisional. Throughout the year as we work with each child, we gain greater and more solid understandings of their abilities, their strengths and weaknesses. Each assessment in isolation is simply another 'snapshot', but it adds to our overall picture.

QCA describe three forms of assessment:

1. **Day-to-day:** this kind of assessment is conducted by teachers and teaching assistants, as well as by children through peer and self-assessment. It can be gleaned from conversations with children about their understanding or through talking with them about their written work. It provides teachers with instantaneous feedback which can result in adjustments to short-term planning.
2. **Periodic:** this assessment takes the form of a review over time of the children's ability to use the skills and understandings they have accrued in their day-to-day learning. Periodic assessment takes the form of evidence gained over this period and can result in changes to medium- and long-term planning. It can inform a teacher's knowledge of a pupil's performance in relation to national standards.
3. **Transitional:** this is the kind of assessment which takes place at the end of a year or key stage. It includes a teacher's assessment of a child's abilities and understandings across the curriculum, as well as results from tests, which help to inform a teacher's assessment of children against national benchmarks. Such summative assessments of children may be collated to provide data about the whole class, and, for local and national monitoring purposes, about the whole school.

In all three cases, assessment should be purposeful and inform future learning and teaching: *Assessment for learning is the process of seeking and interpreting evidence for use by learners and their teachers to decide where the learners are in their learning, where they need to go and how best to get there* ('Research-based principles to guide classroom practice', Assessment Reform Group, 2002).

As such the focus of this *Assessment Kit* is to provide teachers with the tools to obtain and to understand assessment evidence in order to support children in their learning.

Assessment Tasks

These are tasks designed for children working in a small group with the teacher, and include references to the Assessment Foci as part of Assessing Pupils' Progress (APP). It is envisaged that they are used over a period of time so that each child will work in a group on several tasks within a term or even a half term. The tasks enable the teacher to gain a good understanding of the level at which groups of children in general and specific children in particular are working. Achieving a secure understanding of the level at which each child is operating can only be achieved by using these tasks in the ways outlined in introduction to the Assessment Tasks, so it is important to read this carefully.

Review Tasks

These allow teachers to review the performance of the children within a specific mathematical topic, identify common errors and misconceptions, and diagnose any difficulties children may be experiencing. The Review Tasks are written so that they can be used at the start of each topic area. They are therefore an essential part of informing the periodic assessment process.

Assessment Tests

The Assessment Tests, which include mental and written elements, contribute to building a picture of each child's needs for future learning and teaching. The tests complement the periodic assessment of the Assessment Tasks whilst adopting a more formal approach. The Half-term Tests allow the children the opportunity to practice the skills they have learnt in a more formal environment; the End-of-term Tests provide a levelled assessment of each child. The Summer End-of-term Tests allow teachers to conduct a transitional assessment of each child which can be passed on to their next teacher. Each of these tests is accompanied by a diagnostic commentary chart which helps teachers to identify and remedy common misconceptions.

Finally, here are some useful 'Do's and Don'ts of Assessment':

- **Do** start each different topic in teaching maths by reviewing what specific groups of children can and can't do. This will prevent inappropriately targeted lessons.
- **Do** weave the APP-style Assessment Tasks as suggested into the daily and weekly teaching schedule. This prevents you having to allocate time outside the maths lesson for these assessments.
- **Don't** plan the week or fortnight in great detail before the results of the Review Tasks are in! Prior knowledge of the children's specific needs will enable you to maximise the effectiveness of planning time.
- **Don't** think that, on its own, an End-of-term Test provides a secure level for an individual child. Test results must be moderated against the evidence of both teacher's own daily observations and also the results of particular levelled tasks.

These tables summarise the process of Assessment that you might follow in each half term; the *Abacus Evolve* resources that will help you with this; and the outcomes and support they will provide:

Half Term 1		
Process	**Resource**	**Outcome**
Review prior knowledge	*Review Tasks*	Diagnose difficulties and identity misconceptions.
Teach	*Teacher Cards*	Address difficulties and introduce new skills.
Provide differentiated learning activities for groups	*Teacher Cards and I-Planner*	Participate, intervene, observe and record.
Assess	*Assessment Tasks*	Observe and question. Record levels.
Assess	*Half-term Tests*	Practice test. Observe and record.

Half Term 2		
Process	**Resource**	**Outcome**
Review prior knowledge	*Review Tasks*	Diagnose difficulties and identity misconceptions.
Teach	*Teacher Cards*	Address difficulties and introduce new skills.
Provide differentiated learning activities for groups	*Teacher Cards and I-Planner*	Participate, intervene, observe and record.
Assess	*Assessment Tasks*	Observe and question. Record levels.
Assess	*End-of-term Tests*	Record levels.

Produce secure level for individual child based on all the above information

Introduction to the Assessment Tasks

These tasks are designed to provide useful information about the National Curriculum level at which a child is operating. They are designed to be used in conjunction with the National Strategy Assessing Pupils' Progress (APP) materials, alongside the Assessment Guidelines and in line with the Assessment Foci (AFs). How effective these Assessment Tasks are at determining an accurate level for each child depends very much on how they are used. Please read the information below carefully.

Gathering evidence and addressing Assessment Foci

Each of the Assessment Tasks is linked to two or three Assessment Foci within each Attainment Target: AT2 Number, AT3 Shape, Space and Measures and AT4 Handling Data. In most cases there is also reference to one of the three Assessment Foci for AT1 Using and Applying Mathematics (Problem Solving, Communicating and Reasoning) in order for AT1 to be assessed in an integrated way alongside the core content aspects.

The emphasis of these tasks is on providing a depth and quality of evidence about the consistency of a child's performance. No single task can determine that a child is 'Level 3b'. However, witnessing a child working on several tasks over a period of time should provide evidence of their functioning at a particular level mathematically and should also give an indication of their security within that level. If a child is successful in a number of tasks at a particular target level, teachers need to monitor how consistently the evidence applies to the criteria in order to determine whether the child's performance at that level is 'low', 'secure' or 'high'. The extent to which the evidence shows independence and choice, and the range of contexts covered, are also factors in determining a secure level. This evidence should be augmented by the information gained from general observations of each child's verbal engagement and written work in the mathematics classroom.

Making informed decisions

More formal transitional assessments (e.g. the Summer End-of-term Test) along with periodic assessments (e.g. Assessment Tasks and Half-term Tests) can be combined with your day-to-day assessments of the children's understandings (gleaned through following the ***Abacus Evolve*** teaching cards and working with a small group each day) to provide you with a complete assessment package. These three types of assessment – day-to-day, periodic and transitional – should be seen as complementary. Specifically, whenever a child is at the threshold of a particular sub-level in a formal test, evidence from the Assessment Tasks will add security to the judgment. Conversely when a decision about a child's level has been made using teacher assessment, the formal Tests should confirm this. Where children are less successful at the Tasks, the materials provide diagnostic support that can be used to support next steps in planning work for the child.

Using the Tasks in the classroom

The Assessment Tasks can be used in several flexible ways alongside *Abacus Evolve* materials or as a 'stand-alone' resource:

- tasks may be used as small group, adult-led activities during the main part of a lesson
- one task can be used with different groups on different days during a block of work
- specific tasks could be used as part of 'assess and review' lessons
- Other tasks can be used with targeted children only. This is especially useful with children who are performing better than or not as well as expected in more formal tests. In this context, the Assessment Tasks provide complementary evidence to help the moderation of the test result.

Making Assessments

Children can work in a group but it is essential that individual responses are noted. Most tasks start with one or two questions or prompts that draw children into the key concepts. They also include several key questions and things to look for. Teachers need to encourage children to explain what they are doing or to talk through an answer, and then observe closely how children work on the tasks. All these are crucial elements, especially to determine how well the evidence supports assessment of the Using and Applying Assessment Foci.

What the tasks indicate

The 'Most children' description in each task gives evidence that a child is functioning mathematically at the National Curriculum target level of the task. These clear descriptions can, without great difficulty, be matched to observations of children carrying out the task.

Children who meet the requirements of the 'Some children will have progressed further' section are clearly secure at the level of the task, and may in some cases be performing beyond that level, although more evidence from higher-level tasks would be needed to confirm that. It is also the case that tasks from the year group above may be used for more-able pupils.

A child needing support and prompting may be working 'only just' at the task level and, together with any children not able to engage in the task even with support and prompting, will need further practice in the topic along the lines suggested in the Support and Further Practice sections.

If a task uses a + sign (e.g. $L3^{+}$) this indicates that aspects of the content or assessment of children within the task *might* suggest evidence for a higher level. If a task is marked as addressing two levels (e.g. L3/4), then the task has been deliberately written to enable assessment at either level.

Remember:

- Not all children need to do every task: the tasks should be regarded as a bank of activities to be used selectively.
- The tasks help you, the teacher, to gather evidence to support your own professional understanding of each child's level of achievement.
- The tasks allow children to demonstrate achievement at a particular level. The tasks are therefore most useful for children who are likely to be working within that level: consider similar tasks from the year above or below for other children.
- The tasks each focus on a specific and limited number of Assessment Foci – by using a range of tasks evidence can be gathered across the full range of Assessment Foci.
- With appropriate questioning and prompts for children giving explanation most tasks provide evidence for AT1 (Using and Applying) alongside other ATs.
- Tasks should be used alongside the National Strategy APP Guidance and Standards files.
- Tasks will assist with the continuous assessment necessary for diagnosing any difficulties and deciding what to do next. Use the diagnostic information provided with the tasks to help with this process.

Year 2 Assessment Task 1

Counting

- **Assessment Foci:** L2 Number (numbers and number system)
- **Objectives:** ■ Count on or back in 1s or 10s from 2-digit number
- **Suggested Blocks:** A1.a
- **Resources:** 0–99 number square; individual whiteboards and pens; 1–20 number cards; 0–20 number line; 10p and 1p coins

Activity

Revise counting to and from 90 in tens on the number square. Then draw a square in the middle of the board and ask children to copy it onto their whiteboards. Write a 2-digit number in the middle of the square (e.g. *37*) and tell children to copy this also. Then ask children to draw a second square directly below the first and to write the number ten more in the square (*47*). Repeat with a number ten less/one more/one less than 37. When finding ten less, ask: *What number have you have written in your square? How many tens is that? How many ones? Write the number one ten less than 37. How many tens will it have? Which digit stays the same? Why does it stay the same?* Check answers using the number square.

Observe and ask

- *When we count up in tens, what happens to the number?*
- *Which digit changes – the tens or the units?*
- *Why doesn't the units digit change?*
- When finding 10 more than 37, do children write *47* without hesitation or do they write *38*?

Differentiating the task

▼ ***Support:*** Work with numbers 1–50 in the first instance. Use a number line or one-hundred square (fold so only the numbers 0–49 are visible) to direct the counting.

▲ ***Extend:*** Tell children a number, say *47*. Ask them to write the number that is 20 more/20 less. Then ask them to write a number three, four or five more/less than any number up to 100.

Expectations

Most children will be able to write the number ten more and one more than any 2-digit number up to 100. They may find it more difficult to say the number one less, especially when bridging over a decade. If so, it might help to refer to the number square to consolidate their knowledge.

Some children will not have made so much progress and will find it difficult to identify which direction to count on or back – emphasise the forward movement of counting on and backward movement of counting back. These children will also not be aware (or may not make use of the fact) that on a one hundred square the number below any number is 10 more.

Some children will have progressed further and will also be able to find numbers that are 20 or 30 more or less than the original number, and three, four or five more or less. They should be able to explain which digit changes and why.

Further practice

Give each child 15p in 10p and 1p coins. *How much money do you have? If I give you another 10p, how much will you have?* Give them the extra 10p. *So how much do you have now? Were you right?* Refer to the number square. *You had 15p* (point to 15) *and you added on 10p to make 25p.Can you see 25? Where is it? How much do you think you will have if I gave you another 10p? Where will the new number be?* Repeat this up to 55 before practising taking away tens.

Evaluation Notes

Year 2 Assessment Task 2

Problem solving

- **Assessment Foci:** L2 Using and applying (problem solving); L2 Number (numbers and number system)
- **Objectives:** ■ Estimate a number of objects up to 50
- **Suggested Blocks:** A1.b
- **Resources:** counters, cubes, conkers or pasta pieces; plastic (see-through) jugs or other containers; sugar paper and pens

Activity

Prepare several see-through containers containing between 30 and 60 objects (use counters, cubes, conkers or pasta pieces but not a mixture of these). Ask each child to estimate the number of objects in one of the containers. Write down each child's estimate. Carefully pour and spread out the objects onto a piece of sugar paper. Ask children if they want to change their estimate. *Can anyone suggest a way to count the objects?* (***Note:*** since problem solving is one of the foci of this assessment activity, leave it to the children to decide what would be the best way to do this.) After the counting is complete give each child one of the other containers and ask them to repeat the activity – jot down an estimate, pour the objects onto sugar paper and then find an efficient way to count them. Ask children to arrange the objects on the sugar paper in such a way that it makes it easy to count.

Observe and ask

- *How many objects do you think there are?*
- *What would be a good way to count these?*
- *How could you check easily?*
- What strategies do children have for counting?
- How accurate are children's estimates?

Differentiating the task

▼ ***Support:*** Use a smaller number of objects (up to 30). Suggest strategies for counting (e.g. counting in 2s or 5s) and for checking (e.g. arranging the objects systematically on the sugar paper).

▲ ***Extend:*** Give children a larger container and ask them to estimate how many cubes or conkers would fit in it.

Expectations

Most children will be able to make a reasonable estimate of the number of objects in a container – within 10 or 15 of the actual number is reasonable. They should have some strategies for counting efficiently (e.g. counting in 2s or 5s). They should also have strategies for arranging the objects on the sugar paper (e.g. in groups of 5 or 10 or in straight lines), which make it easier for them to check their estimate. Some may need prompting to use these types of strategy but will appreciate the value of using them.

Some children will not have made so much progress and will make estimates that are inaccurate (e.g. over 100). They will count objects one-by-one moving them from one place to another without ordering them systematically; consequently they may lose track of their count.

Some children will have progressed further and will realise the need to have systematic approaches to counting the objects, which they will be able to articulate. Their estimates will be thoughtful (e.g. they may think about how many cubes fit across the container and the number of layers of cubes there are).

Further practice

Children struggling need to have more structured opportunities to arrange objects into 2s, 5s and 10s and discuss how such arrangements aid counting. They should do this for up to 100 objects.

Evaluation Notes

Year 2 Assessment Task 3

Tens and units

- **Assessment Foci:** L2+ Number (numbers and number system)
- **Objectives:** ■ Know what each digit in a 2-digit number represents, including 0 as a place holder ■ Partition 2-digit numbers into T and U
- **Suggested Blocks:** A1.c
- **Resources:** 0–99 number cards; £1, 10p and 1p coins; 0–99 number square; individual whiteboards and pens; hundreds, tens and units place-value cards

Activity

Shuffle the number cards 30–99 and give one to each child. Ask children to read their number and say how many tens and how many units it has. Challenge them to make the matching amount with 10p and 1p coins. Check that they do match. (***Note:*** the coins provide a context for manipulating number – there is no need to focus on the monetary amount.) If necessary, refer to the number square to help by saying: *Point to your number. Now point to the number ten bigger.* Repeat, making numbers ten bigger/smaller, then one bigger/smaller. *Which coin could you use to make your number ten bigger?* Then give each pair a set of tens and units place-value cards. *Make 20 from your cards. How many tens do you need? How many ones? How can you make your number ten bigger? What is your new number? How will you make your number six bigger?*

Observe and ask

- *What is your number?*
- *Which number is the tens number? Which is the units number?*
- *How will you match the 10p and 1p coins to the number on your card?*
- Do they count the 10p coins first?
- Do they write the number that is ten bigger correctly?
- Can they solve problems that involve bridging the tens?
- *Can you make the number one bigger? Which digit will you change?*
- Do they add an extra unit when making a number one bigger?

Differentiating the task

▼ ***Support:*** Show children a number card e.g. 21. *Can you make 21p? How many 10p/1p coins do you need? How would you make your number 1p bigger? How much do you have now? Can you find the number on the number square?* Repeat this up to 29p. *Which number is one bigger?* (30) *How many tens are there in 30? How many ones?* Continue the activity, bridging over ten, e.g. 29, 30, 31 for practice.

▲ ***Extend:*** Use place-value cards to make 3-digit numbers, and ask children to match £1, 10p and 1p coins to the cards. *Take 20 away. What is your new number? Is your new number bigger or smaller than original one?* Repeat, increasing/ decreasing numbers by 100, 10 and 1.

Expectations

Most children will be able to read the number cards and should be able to tell you how many tens and units is in each number. However, check that they point to the correct digit when saying tens and units digits. They should know that in multiples of ten, the zero establishes that there are only tens and no units, but it can be useful to use the coins to reinforce this. Most will be able to match the 10p and 1p coins to the total, and should be able to say and write the number ten bigger. They may sometimes get confused when the digits of the original number are the same (e.g. *44*).

Some children will not have made so much progress and will struggle to consistently identify the number of tens and units in a two-digit number. The support task addresses this by supporting children in relating the numbers to 10p and 1p coins. Reinforce this by asking: *How many 10p pieces would you need to make 20p? How many ones?* Point to the tens or units digits as you ask the questions. ***Note:*** some of these children may find it easier to add and subtract tens than to add and subtract ones.

Some children will have progressed further and will also be able to use HTU place-value cards. Increasing/decreasing 3-digit numbers by 100, 10 and 1 and explaining in each case which digit changes and why is indicative of Level 3.

Further practice

Write on the board three consecutive numbers, for example: *26, 27, 28.* Say: *Read the numbers with me.* Emphasise the *twenty* as you say the words, e.g. ***Twenty**-six. Make this number with your place-value cards. How many tens have you used? How did you know how many to tens to use? How many units?* Point to *27. What will you need to do to make twenty-seven? Which digit do you change? Why?* Repeat.

Evaluation Notes

Year 2 Assessment Task 4

Addition and subtraction strategies

- **Assessment Foci:** L2 Using and applying (problem solving; communicating); L2 Number (solving numerical problems)
- **Objectives:** ■ Add by counting on in 1s from the larger number, crossing a multiple of 10 ■ Recognise addition as counting on ■ Add three numbers by putting the largest number first ■ Recognise that addition can be done in any order ■ Use the + and = signs to record addition sentences
- **Suggested Blocks:** B1.a; B1.b
- **Resources:** PCM B (one copy per child); pencil and paper (or whiteboards and pens)

Activity

Ask children some questions which involve adding three single-digit numbers, e.g. *What is 5 and 4 and 2? What is 3 and 4 and 8?* Discuss different ways these numbers could be added together. Give children a copy of PCM B. Ask them to write the numbers *8*, *15* and *6* in the corner circles of one of the triangles. They should add the numbers together and put the answer in the centre. They can use paper and pencil or whiteboards to record their calculations. They should put the same three numbers in the corner of a second triangle and add them a different way, working either in pairs or individually. Give children further sets of three numbers (choose ones that children should be able to solve) to put in the corners and again ask children to solve these questions in two different ways.

Now ask children to put the number *20* in the centre of the triangle and numbers *7* and *5* in two of its corners. *What number would go in the third corner?* Repeat with other numbers at the centre and at two of the three corners.

Observe and ask

- *What would be a good way to add those numbers?*
- *Can you add them in another way?*
- *What number is missing? How can you find out what it is?*
- Do children choose efficient methods to find the missing number?
- Can children explain their choice of strategies?

Differentiating the task

▼ ***Support:*** Work with numbers totalling no more than 20 and let children have cubes or counters for support.

▲ ***Extend:*** Choose a number for the centre of the triangle, e.g. *35*, and ask children to find different combinations of three numbers that will produce this total.

Expectations

Most children will be able to add three numbers together using a range of calculation strategies (e.g. putting the largest number first). They will use 10 and other decade numbers to support counting on as well as other known facts (e.g. they might add 8, 15 and 6 as 15 + 14 because they know that 8 and 6 are 14 and they can then use a near double). Where they do not have such strategies they should still be able to find answers accurately by using an empty number line to support with counting on. These children are aware that addition can be done in any order. They should also be able to record calculations using appropriate signs and should be able to discuss their choice of strategies using appropriate mathematical vocabulary.

Some children will not have made so much progress and will not always choose the most efficient strategies. They may revert to counting on in ones for each of the numbers. They will find the second task (where one of the three numbers is missing) difficult because of the number of steps involved. They may not always record accurately or use signs in the right place.

Some children will have progressed further and will use a variety of strategies as well as being able to discuss the relative merits of different ways of solving a problem. They should be able to find a range of solutions to the extension task.

Further practice

Children struggling need more practice adding three numbers. They should be encouraged to look for the most efficient way of doing this, rather than simply adding in the order in which the numbers are presented.

Evaluation Notes

Year 2 Assessment Task 5

Adding three numbers

- **Assessment Foci:** L2 Using and applying (communicating); L2 Number (mental methods)
- **Objectives:** ■ Recognise that addition can be done in any order
- **Suggested Blocks:** B1.b
- **Resources:** three large 1–6 spotted dice; individual whiteboards and pens; three 1–6 numbered dice (cover 1, 2 and 3 on one of the dice with 7, 8 and 9); 1–50 number cards

Activity

Explain to children that you are going to throw three spotted dice and that you want them to write down the total amount of the three sets of spots. Point out that you will be asking them to explain the strategy they used for totalling. After doing this several times, switch to using numbered dice and observe and discuss the strategies children use.

Observe and ask

- *How many dots can you see?* (e.g. *six, five* and *four.*)
- *What strategy did you use?* Can children add up the spots and give a total? (e.g. *6 + 4 = 10 and 5 more makes 15.*)
- *Did anyone use a different method to add the dice spots?* (e.g. *Double 6 is 12, take away 1 is 11, add 4 is 15* or *Double 5 is 10, add 1 is 11, add 4 is 15* or *I put 6 in my head, counted on 5 and then counted on 4 more.*
- *What strategies did you use to add up the three numbers on the dice? Did you use any different strategies?*

Differentiating the task

▼ ***Support:*** Add two 1-digit numbers only with this group. Ask children to throw the spotted dice and identify the same numbers on numbered dice. Ask: *Which is the bigger number?* (e.g. 5) *Remember that number. Which is the smaller number?* (e.g. 4) *Show me this with your fingers. Remember to put the number five in your head. Now count on the four you've shown me with your four fingers: six, seven, eight, nine*. Repeat.

▲ ***Extend:*** Use one 1–6 and one 4–9 numbered dice, and a set of number cards 1–50. Throw the two dice and select a number card at random. *Add up the numbers* (e.g. *23, 8, 5*). Discuss strategies, such as: *23 + 8 = 31* (because 23 + 7 = 30, add 1 = 31), *31 + 5 = 36* (1 + 5 = 6 and 30 + 6 = 36). They may say *3 + 5 = 8, double 8 = 16, so 20 + 16 = 36.*

Expectations

Most children will use their knowledge of number bonds to answer and so switching to numbered dice should not be a problem. Most children will be comfortable working with number bonds quite quickly, and they can then be encouraged to use doubling or trebling a number as an alternative strategy. These children should show awareness of the variety of strategies available to them and be able to discuss these using appropriate vocabulary.

Some children will not have made so much progress and will find it difficult to add together two numbered dice without resorting to counting on fingers since they lack the requisite number-bond knowledge. They need to be encouraged to make the connection between the number of dots (i.e. a physical representation) and the abstract symbols of numbers. They then need to be encouraged to use known facts (e.g. doubles) and strategies, such as starting with the larger number and counting on, to solve these problems.

Some children will have progressed further and will be able to total three 1-digit numbers, or two 1-digit numbers and a 2-digit number. This group should be able to add two single-digit numbers on a dice and a 2-digit number card e.g. 5 and 6 on the dice and the number card 35. Discussing the strategies that can be used is essential because they will vary depending on the calculation.

Further practice

Using a 1–6 and a 4–9 numbered dice, throw two numbers. Establish which is the larger number and ask children to use fingers to count on the smaller number. Before counting on, ask children to check if the calculation involves a number bond to ten. There are several bonds for ten and it is important to encourage children to recognise them.

Evaluation Notes

Year 2 Assessment Task 6

Addition and subtraction problems

- **Assessment Foci:** L2 Using and applying (reasoning); L2 Number (solving numerical problems; written methods)
- **Objectives:** ■ Use the +, - and = signs to record addition and subtraction sentences
- **Suggested Blocks:** B1.c; B1.d
- **Resources:** one jar or tin; up to 20 cubes or conkers per child; pencil and paper (or whiteboards and pens)

Activity

Show children + , - and = signs on flashcards. Check that they can read each one and know what it signifies; if they are unable to do this then they are not ready for this assessment. Count 6 conkers into a jar. Now put in 3 more. *How many altogether? What could you write down to show what we have done?* For this first example, if necessary, model writing the number sentence, *6 + 3 = 9*. Now take 2 conkers out of the jar. *How many are left? How can this be recorded?* Repeat with two or three further examples. If appropriate, extend children to independently recording number sentences beyond 10. Now give all children some cubes and a container and ask them to make up some problems like this of their own, recording their problems in number sentences.

Observe and ask

- *How many cubes are in the jar now? How do you know?*
- *Can you write a number sentence to show that?*
- Do children write appropriate number sentences using the operation signs correctly?
- *You have written… 4 + 3 = 7. Can you explain that with the cubes?*

Differentiating the task

▼ ***Support:*** Take a more structured approach focussing on one operation at a time. Another supportive strategy you can employ is to give children half-finished sentences to complete, e.g. *4 +□ ?□*.

▲ ***Extend:*** Extend to simple multiplication (as repeated addition) – put 2 conkers into the jar, then another 2, then another 2, then another 2.

Expectations

Most children will be able to do the arithmetic involved in this activity and record a number sentence for each of the operations. They may occasionally miss one of the signs, for example, recording *5 + 3 8*, or sometimes put a sign in the wrong place, for example *5 3 + = 8*. They will be able to create their own number sentences and explain the operations they have written down using the cubes and appropriate mathematical vocabulary.

Some children will not have made so much progress and will have difficulty recording the number sentences accurately. They may just write down the numbers involved and show a lack of understanding of the operations represented by the signs. They may not be accurate in answering the questions.

Some children will have progressed further and will also write accurate number sentences, explaining how these relate to the modelling of addition and subtraction.

Further practice

Children struggling should repeat this with smaller numbers drawing pictures of the conkers alongside the number sentences.

Evaluation Notes

Year 2 Assessment Task 7

Measuring and comparing length using centimetres

- **Assessment Foci:** L2 Using and applying (problem solving); L2 Shape, space and measures (measures)
- **Objectives:** ■ Estimate, measure and compare lengths using standard units: centimetres
- **Suggested Blocks:** C1.a
- **Resources:** salt dough; infant centimetre rulers; centicubes (Multibase units); individual whiteboards and pens; red and blue strips of paper

Activity

Give each child a lump of salt dough and an infant ruler. Take time to look at the ruler and establish that each demarcation is one centimetre, that each centimetre is exactly the same length and that it is the demarcation *after* the number and not the space in between that is used to establish the length. Ask the children to make one salt-dough snake 15cm long and another 9cm long.

Observe and ask

- *How long is your ruler?*
- *What units do you use the ruler to measure in?*
- *Are all the centimetres the same length?*
- *Can you point to where you will begin measuring?* (Check that they are pointing to the base line.)
- *If your snake was six centimetres long, show me where he would start and finish on your ruler.*
- *Make a 15cm-long snake and a 9cm-long snake.*
- *Which is the longer?*
- *How much longer? How do you know?*

Differentiating the task

▼ ***Support:*** Allow this group to use centicubes to count on the difference in their snake lengths. When children are confident with this, practise measuring with the ruler, reinforcing how to use the ruler correctly and emphasising the correct vocabulary.

▲ ***Extend:*** Give these children the problem of making two snakes with a difference in length of 4cm – that is, one needs to be 4cm longer or shorter than the other. Children can then make more snakes with a difference of 4cm, before moving on to make three or more snakes, each with a difference of 3cm.

Expectations

Most children will be able to make the snakes and measure them accurately. They may initially make the snakes by estimating and be able to adjust the length using the ruler. Some may measure up to the number on the ruler (to a halfway number) but not up to the demarcation *after* the number. Some will measure to the demarcation *before* the number and some will not align the snake with the base line. However, all these children should recognise these errors and correct them once they are pointed out. They will also be able to say which snake is longer and which is shorter and, with prompting, will be able to find the difference.

Some children will not have made so much progress and will struggle to use a ruler accurately. They may only be able to make snakes which are approximately the same length, and will need help measuring. This group will tend to make their snakes and then think about how to measure them, rather than trying to make snakes with an idea of the required lengths in mind. These children are also less likely to be able to adjust the length of their snakes to a particular length. Help them to find the difference by asking: *Which is the longer snake?* Show them how to place both snakes on a base line before using centicubes to work out the difference. ***Note:*** when using centicubes, make sure children join them together properly so that there are no gaps and the lines aren't 'wiggly'.

Some children will have progressed further and will find it easy to make the snakes and to find the difference. They will also be able to problem solve by successfully making snakes of a given difference in length. This is a challenging activity because children are often looking for the one *right* answer, so the open nature of the activity is quite tricky. When they have completed the task, say: *Show me the difference. Is it (4cm)?* Encourage children to compare their answers by looking at the pairs of numbers.

Further practice

Ask children to cut strips of paper, one red strip 6cm long and one blue strip 9cm long. *How did you measure them? Which is the longer? How much longer is it?* Encourage children to use centicubes to measure the difference between the two strips.

Evaluation Notes

Year 2 Assessment Task 8

Shape properties

- **Assessment Foci:** L2 Using and applying (reasoning); L2 Shape, space and measures (properties of shape)
- **Objectives:** ■ Use the names of common 2D shapes, including: pentagon, hexagon, octagon ■ Sort 2D shapes and describe their features: number of sides and corners ■ Classify and describe common 2D and 3D shapes
- **Suggested Blocks:** D1.a (also B3.a)
- **Resources:** PCM D (one sheet per child cut up, ideally photocopied to A3 size); plastic shapes; sugar paper

Activity

Spread some plastic shapes on the floor and, in turn, ask each child to choose a shape and, without indicating which one it is, describe its properties. The other children should try to work out which one it is. Show children PCM D and ask them which of the shapes are like the plastic ones and which ones are different. For those that are seen as 'different' can children identify any shared characteristics? Establish that shapes can be sorted by the number of sides they have e.g. triangles, quadrilaterals (including squares and rectangles), pentagons, hexagons and octagons. Check children know how many sides each of these shapes have. Cut up the sheet and ask children to stick the shapes on sugar paper under the headings *triangles, quadrilaterals, pentagons, hexagons, octagons.*

Note: an alternative way to present the task would be to ask children to find for each shape on the sheet, one other shape that would go in the same group, and draw a line to link them.

Observe and ask

- *How can you describe that shape?*
- *What can you tell me about that shape that is similar or different to that one?*
- *How could you sort the shapes?*
- Do children identify properties of different shapes?
- Can children sort the shapes on the sheet according to their number of sides/corners?

Differentiating the task

▼ ***Support:*** Have all of the vocabulary, both names of shapes and words to describe their properties on flashcards for children to refer to.

▲ ***Extend:*** Challenge children to draw some further irregular pentagons, hexagons and octagons.

Expectations

Most children will be able to use a range of appropriate mathematical vocabulary to describe shapes and be able to give examples of similarities and differences. They should be able to group most of the shapes on the sheet although they may occasionally miscount the number of sides of the pentagons, hexagons and octagons. They should appreciate that all of the different shapes have regular and irregular versions and ought not be confused by the varied orientations of some of the shapes.

Some children will not have made so much progress and will find it difficult to give concise descriptions of shapes. They may be confused by irregular shapes, particularly ones with concave features.

Some children will have progressed further and will also give concise explanations of the similarities and differences between shapes. They will identify and describe a range of their features (e.g. symmetry as well as the more obvious number of sides/corners). They will be able to quickly match shapes which share the same property.

Further practice

Children struggling need more opportunities to have physical experience of shapes. They should be prompted to describe similarities and differences between shapes. They should have vocabulary lists to refer to when working with shapes.

Evaluation Notes

Year 2 Assessment Task 9

Subtracting

- **Assessment Foci:** L2 Number (mental methods; written methods)
- **Objectives:** ■ Count back in 1s, not crossing a multiple of 10 ■ Extend understanding of subtraction as taking away
- **Suggested Blocks:** D1.c; D1.d
- **Resources:** 10p and 1p coins; individual whiteboards and pens; 0–99 number squares; tens and units place-value cards; purses

Activity

Write a subtraction on the board involving taking a 1-digit number from a 2-digit number, such as *24 – 4 =*. *What have I written?* Encourage as many different responses as possible, for example: *24 take away four/24 subtract four/make 24 four smaller/count back four from 24*. Then ask: *What is the answer? How did you work it out?* ***Note:*** children who are still counting back will find this assessment difficult and so you may like to model the subtraction with 10p and 1p coins. Now write *24 – 6* on the board. *How many to get back to 20? (4) How many more to take away? (2) What is the answer?* Write *34 – 4 =* and *34 – 5 =* on the board, and ask children to complete the number sentences. Discuss strategies children used.

Observe and ask

- *Who can read what I have written?*
- *How can you write and complete the number sentence? How did you work out the*
- *answer?*
- Do they say: *I used five fingers and I counted back* or *I know that 24 – 4 is 20 so 24 – 6 will be taking two more away, so that is 18.*
- *Who can answer 34 – 4? How did you work it out?*
- *What about 34 – 5? How did you work it out?*

Differentiating the task

▼ ***Support:*** These children will find it useful to model each subtraction they work on with 10p and 1p coins. Continue to work with them as they subtract 1-digit numbers from any 2-digit number to get back to a multiple of ten (i.e. not crossing the tens), e.g. *15 – 5 = 10*.

▲ ***Extend:*** Give each child a number square to work out calculations that involve subtracting of 1-digit numbers from 2-digit numbers and crossing the tens, for example: *37 – 8* or *47 – 8*. Discuss the two-step operation children used. Consolidate this but also ask questions to confirm that children are using the two-step operation. Look for patterns and relationships, for example: *If 47 – 8 = 39, what will 57 – 8 be? What about 107 – 8?*

Expectations

Most children will be able to count back in ones, and bridging over the ten should also be easy. However, in this assessment you are trying to establish whether they can split the single digit number into meaningful parts in order to get to a multiple of ten before subtracting the remaining part. This is why it is important to encourage children to explain what they are doing. They should be able to do this for different multiples of ten, not just to 20.

Some children will not have made so much progress and will struggle to deal with subtraction abstractly. They may only be able to take away back to a multiple of ten with 10p and 1p coins – that is, they can solve *24 – 4* but not *24 – 5*. These children find the written form of subtraction number sentences much harder to understand than the spoken form and can become very confused. When representing an addition sentence using coins, they are able to represent both written parts of the addition with physical objects (e.g. for 12p + 5p, they can 'make' both parts of the addition using coins – a group of coins which make up 12p and a group which represent 5p – before adding them together). However, when performing a subtraction (e.g. 12p – 5p), they can only 'make' the first number (12p). It is vital, therefore, that you talk through the procedure to help overcome this problem, rather than trying to make them understand the written form.

Some children will have progressed further and will also be able to use two-step operations to subtract larger single-digit numbers from 2-digit numbers whilst bridging the tens. These children will use their knowledge of number bonds to split the single-digit number into two appropriate parts (firstly to get to a multiple of ten and then to reach the answer) in order to solve such subtraction problems. These children will therefore be able to work with the full range of single-digit numbers.

Further practice

Write on the board the subtraction number sentences *20 – 4 =, 10 – 4 =, 20 – 5 =* and *10 – 5 =*. Encourage children to use ten toes and ten fingers to make 20 and practise taking away from 20. *Show me 20 take away four. How many are left? Now add on four. How many now?*

Evaluation Notes

Understanding doubling and halving

- **Assessment Foci:** L2 Number (operations, relationships)
- **Objectives:** ■ Recognise halving as the inverse of doubling
- **Suggested Blocks:** E1.a
- **Resources:** 10p, 5p and 1p coins; individual whiteboards and pens; dominoes; 1–50 number cards; 1–6 dice

Activity

Use fingers to double/halve up to ten. Put your thumbs together and say: *One plus one is two*. Then pull them apart, saying: *Half of two is one*. Repeat up to five plus five. Then give children two 5p and eight 1p coins. Ask them to make amounts up to 18p. Ask children to make 6p add 6p (5p + 1p and 5p + 1p). Continue up to 9p + 9p (5p + four 1p coins and 5p + four 1p coins). Always say the inverse e.g. *if 7p + 7p (double 7p) is 14p, what is half of 14p?*

Observe and ask

- *Can you show me double four (four plus four) with your fingers? Can you write the answer?*
- *Can you show me half of eight? Can you write the answer?*
- *Can you make 10p with your coins?*
- Do children arrange the coins in pairs (so they can see the halves more easily)?
- Do they remember to use the 5p pieces?
- *Can you show me half of 10p? Can you write the answer?*
- *How much is double five? Double five is the same as five plus five. Can you write the answer?*
- *Can you halve 12p and write down the answer? Can you double your answer and write it down?*

Differentiating the task

▼ ***Support:*** Use three sets of domino doubles, placed face down on the table, to find doubles up to 6 + 6. Children take turns to pick one domino up. If they can say the number sentence, e.g. *Five plus five equals ten*, they win 10p.

▲ ***Extend:*** Check that this group can double multiples of ten to 100 using their fingers, and know the associated halves, assuming each finger/thumb has a value of ten. Children take turns to pick a number card 1–50. If they can say the doubling and halving sentences correctly, they win 20p. For example, if a child picks 24, he/she should say: *Half 24 is 12; double 12 is 24*. ***Note:*** if children pick an odd number card, they should always double the number first, then halve it. Next write *22, 24, 26* on the board. Ask children to double each number and to describe their strategies. Ensure coins are available to help them. Do they automatically use existing knowledge to work out the answer? Some will use coins because they are there; others will double, having partitioned first.

Expectations

Most children will be able to halve and double up to ten, especially if they are encouraged to use fingers (the finger exercise helps children to memorise halving and doubling up to ten). These children will know doubles up to 6 + 6 and 10 + 10, and associated halves. They should be able to derive 7 + 7, 8 + 8, and 9 + 9 by relating to other known facts, e.g. using 10 + 10 = 20 to work out 9 + 9 (i.e. using the fact that 9 is one less than 10). They should demonstrate some understanding of the relationship between doubling and halving.

Some children will not have made so much progress and will find halving and doubling up to ten difficult without significant visual prompt such as dominoes. Using dominoes, they should be able to find all the doubles in a set of dominoes, up to 6 + 6. They will also be able to pick up a double and to say it as a number sentence, e.g. *Five plus five equals ten/Half of ten is five*. Encourage this group to use fingers to check doubles up to 5 + 5 but discourage counting the fingers or counting on.

Some children will have progressed further and will also be able to double and halve tens to 50 + 50 = 100, reinforcing this with their fingers. They should be familiar with near doubles such as 6 + 5 and 60 + 50 as they will be able to work out new number facts using existing knowledge. These children understand the relationship between doubling and halving – that is, if double 22 is 44, then half of 44 is 22. These children may be able to establish this using a two-step operation and partitioning. For example when working out 7 + 7, these children know 5 + 5 and 2 + 2 so they can find out 7 + 7. This is especially helpful when doubling 2-digit numbers. These children need to know important doubles and halves, such as 50 + 50 and 25 + 25.

Further practice

Play doubling bingo by writing even numbers up to 12 on the board. Children choose and write down three. Throw a dice and children double the number shown. If they have the answer, it is crossed out. The first to cross out all three numbers shouts *Bingo!*

Evaluation Notes

Year 2 Assessment Task 11

Addition and subtraction problems with money

- **Assessment Foci:** L2 Using and applying (reasoning); L2 Number (solving numerical problems; written methods)
- **Objectives:** ■ Recognise all coins and begin to use £.p notation for money ■ Solve 'real-life' problems involving money (paying an exact sum) ■ Solve problems involving addition, subtraction, multiplication or division in contexts of numbers, measures or pounds and pence
- **Suggested Blocks:** E1.c; E1.d
- **Resources:** PCM A (cut into 8 cards: one set per child) or label 8 physical toys with the prices on PCM A; selection of coins; 100 number line

Activity

Check that children can identify coins and also understand how smaller and larger value coins can be exchanged, for example *a 10p coin is equivalent to two 5p coins, five 2p coins or ten 1p coins*. Hold up a toy with a price label or use one of the teddy bears on PCM A. Ask children to suggest different coins that could be used to pay for it. Now ask children to select any two of the toys/teddy bears and find the total cost. They should repeat this four times for different pairs of toys or teddy bears. Children may use the coins for support or record as number sentences as appropriate. Next tell children they have 50p (hold a 50p piece) to spend on any toy/teddy. *How much change would you get?* Repeat four times using different toys/teddies.

Observe and ask

- *What coins would you use to pay for that toy/teddy?*
- *How much would those two toys/teddies cost altogether? How can you be sure?*
- *How much change from 50p for that toy/teddy? How can you be sure?*
- Can children find total costs or change from 50p?
- Can they record/explain this correctly?

Differentiating the task

▼ ***Support:*** Use toys/teddies 5-8 (*30p, 20p, 35p, 25p*) only for the addition and subtraction tasks. These are each priced in multiples of 5 and so can be paid for more easily.

▲ ***Extend:*** Find the total cost of three toys/teddies and find change from £1 or £2.

Expectations

Most children will be able to confidently identify different coins and know which to use to buy different items. They should be able to find the total cost of any pair of toys/teddies and record the calculation in a number sentence, possibly using partitioning strategies. They should be able to find the change from 50p by counting on (shopkeeper's addition) or by subtracting from 50 on a number line. They should be able to explain their methods at each stage.

Some children will not have made so much progress and will not always choose the most appropriate coins to pay for an item (e.g. using all 10p and 1p coins rather than 5p and 2p coins). When finding the total cost of two toys/teddies they may not use specific calculation strategies. They may also find it difficult to record their calculation and explain their methods. Finding change may be difficult because they have not understood how to solve subtraction problems by counting on, recognising subtraction only as *taking away*. These children may find this *taking away* method difficult to do from 50.

Some children will have progressed further and will also confidently find the cost of several items and change from £1 or £2. They will use a variety of calculation strategies that work best for the numbers they are dealing with and be able to explain how they are choosing to solve the problems.

Further practice

Children struggling need to have more opportunities to play shopkeeper and customer with real coins and real objects, buying two items and finding out how much they need to pay using coins. They also need practice in finding change using the shopkeeper's addition method.

Evaluation Notes

Year 2 Assessment Task 12

Compare numbers

- **Assessment Foci:** L2+ Using and applying (reasoning); L2+ Number (numbers and number system)
- **Objectives:** ■ Compare two or more 2-digit numbers; introduce the greater than (>), less than (<) signs ■ Say a number lying between two numbers, up to at least 100
- **Suggested Blocks:** A2.d
- **Resources:** 1–100 number cards; Post-It Notes; 0–100 number line

Activity

Shuffle number cards 1–100, and give each child four cards. Ask them to arrange their numbers in order. Children should take turns to read their order aloud. Invite each child to choose the largest and smallest number and put aside the other two cards. Then ask them to write an 'in-between' number on a Post-It Note and to place it between their two cards.

Observe and ask

- *How will you arrange your cards in order?*
- Do they arrange the cards correctly?
- *Did you find any cards difficult to order? Which cards? Why?*
- *Can you explain why you put this card here?*
- *Which card was the most difficult to position? Why?*
- *Can you write a number that comes between your two cards? Is there another number you could have written?*
- Do children look at the tens numbers first?
- When comparing numbers in the same decade, do children compare the units digits?

Differentiating the task

▼ ***Support:*** Use number cards in the range 1–30 and ask children to order three cards only. *Which is the biggest/smallest number? Has it any tens? How many units? The first number to be ordered is the first one you come to when counting. How do you know that this number is in between?*

▲ ***Extend:*** Write on the board a row of six numbers between 50 and 550, such as *204* and *240*, *56* and *65*, *378* and *387*. Check that children are able to read each number. *How will you order your numbers? How do you know that you have ordered them all?* (Point to a number in a child's order.) *How do you know that this number is in the right place? Write a number that comes between these two numbers.*

Expectations

Most children will be able to arrange their cards in order and be able to explain their reasons for arranging them, for example by referring first to the tens and then the units. They should be able to identify other numbers between two numbers and realise that more than one answer is possible to this question.

Some children will not have made so much progress and will need to reinforce ordering with smaller numbers. ***Note:*** always use a 0–100 number line to explain ordering rather than a number square, in which the numbers at the ends of lines are physically separated. Check that children are able to read each number. Are they able to read the 'teen' numbers? Do they know that 1-digit numbers are smaller than 2-digit numbers? (Some may think that 8 or 9 are bigger than a teen number, because the teen number starts with a 1.)

Some children will have progressed further and will also be able to order 3-digit numbers. They will find it easy to order the numbers but may need help with being systematic. For example: *When you have written a number, cross it out. How do you know that this is the smallest number? How did you know which was the smaller of these two numbers?* These children may think that an in-between number is the halfway number between any two numbers. Children working comfortably with the ordering of 3-digit numbers are showing evidence of L3 for this Assessment Focus.

Further practice

Hand out random number cards up to 30 and ask each child to read their number. *Who has the smallest/biggest number? You two, pretend you are door posts. Which numbers can stand between the door posts in the right order? How do you know you are in the right place?* Refer to the number line for support.

Evaluation Notes

Year 2 Assessment Task 13

Pairs to 10

- **Assessment Foci:** L2 Number (mental methods)
- **Objectives:** ■ Rehearse addition and subtraction facts for pairs of numbers that total up to 10 ■ Begin to add three 1-digit numbers mentally
- **Suggested Blocks:** B2.a; B2.b
- **Resources:** 10p coins; a tin; several sets of 1–9 number cards; individual whiteboards and pens; cubes; a cloth; 0–20 number line

Activity

Revise addition pairs for 10. As you count out ten 1p coins, ask children to match the count with their fingers. Then drop some coins into a tin one at a time, without letting children see. Children listen carefully to the sound of the coins and count them quietly, perhaps using their fingers. They then write down the number of coins left.

On the board, write *5 + ? = 10*. Ask children to write and answer the number sentence by counting on using their fingers. Repeat a few times, dropping different numbers of coins into the tin.

Give each child three number cards (two of which must add up to 10, e.g. 4, 5 and 6 or 7, 4 and 3). *I would like you to add the three numbers*. Check their addition strategy – do they look for pairs to 10? Repeat with at least two more sets of cards, making sure the trios are mixed up (i.e. the pairs that add to 10 are not adjacent).

Observe and ask

- *How many coins are in the tin? How do you know?*
- Are children able to explain how they found the answer?
- Can they read the number sentence on the board?
- *Can you show me how you added the three numbers?*
- When adding three numbers, do children look for pairs that make 10?
- *Can you show me the two cards that make 10?*
- *Can you add on the extra number? What do you get?*
- Do they know the answer or do they count on the extra number?
- *Can you write the number sentence?*

Differentiating the task

▼ ***Support:*** Use cubes and play the memory game. Count out ten cubes in two rows of five and cover one set of five cubes with a cloth. *How many cubes can you see? How many are hidden? How do you know?* Always check that children are correct and say the number sentence. Repeat to create other number sentences.

▲ ***Extend:*** Give these children a number sentence with two unknowns, for example: □ + □ + 6 = 16. Read out the number sentence: *Something and something add six makes 16* or *Six and something and something makes 16. What could the somethings be?* Repeat with other similar sentences.

Expectations

Most children will be able to identify the number pairs for 10 using their fingers. For example: *There are ten 1p coins* (child shows ten fingers), *six went into the tin* (child bends down six fingers). *So there must be four left in the tin: 6 + 4 = 10.* When given three cards, each child should immediately identify the pairs that make 10, demonstrating their knowledge of addition facts. Most of these children should be able to add 10 and a one-digit number mentally using place-value understanding.

Some children will not have made so much progress and will still be finding it difficult to remember the pairs that make ten. They are often reluctant to use their fingers to help with the activity. Encourage visualising ten in two rows of five. It is then easier to see how many are missing. In this grouping there are two missing.

O O O O O
O O O

It is important that children say the number sentence each time, e.g. *Eight and two more make ten.*

Some children will have progressed further and will also use their knowledge of number pairs to solve problems using unknowns. You may need to ask extra questions to get them started. Usually rephrasing will be enough. *Six and something makes 16. What could the something be?* (10) *But we need two numbers, so which two numbers could we use? Can you think of any other pairs that we could use?* Try other unknowns to consolidate their understanding of adding on a single-digit number to ten, e.g. 6 + 4 + □ = 15.

Further practice

Play a game of pelmanism with digit cards 1–9 (with two 5s) in which children have to find pairs that total 10. The range of numbers can be increased, e.g. to 14 and children can find pairs that make 15.

Evaluation Notes

Year 2 Assessment Task 14

Recognising right angles

- **Assessment Foci:** L2 Using and applying (communicating); L2 Shape, space and measures (properties of position and movement)
- **Objectives:** ■ Recognise whole, half and quarter turns ■ Know that a right angle is a measure of a quarter turn ■ Recognise right angles in simple shapes ■ Recognise clockwise and anticlockwise turns
- **Suggested Blocks:** B2.c; B2.d
- **Resources:** PCM C; markers; plastic shapes

Activity

Show children some plastic shapes (e.g. squares, triangles, pentagons, rectangles). Check that they know what a right angle is and which of the shapes in front of them have one or more right angles. You could sort the shapes to show which have right angles and which do not. Remind children how to make a right-angle checker by folding a piece of paper in half and then in half again. They should use the right-angle checker to find the right angles in the shapes. Give each child a copy of PCM C. This could be cut up so that each shape arrangement can be considered separately and, for some children, enlarged. Ask children to use their right-angle checker to find all of the right angles on each shape, marking the corners where they find these with a marker.

Note: There are 9 right angles on the top shape arrangement and 12 (including 2 external ones) on the lower shape arrangement.

Observe and ask

- *Can you describe a right angle?*
- *Which shapes have right angles?*
- *How can you use the right-angle checker?*
- Do children correctly identify the right angles in the two shape arrangements?

Differentiating the task

▼ ***Support:*** Number each of the corners in the shape arrangements. Systematically go through the corners checking children are using right-angle checker correctly.

▲ ***Extend:*** Give children a square piece of paper, ruler and pencil. Ask them to create their own shape arrangement that could be checked by a friend for right angles.

Expectations

Most children will be able to recall what a right angle looks like and which shapes have one or more. They should be able to locate most of the right angles on the shape arrangements. They may need prompting to spot those that are not in horizontal-vertical orientations and those that are external to the shapes in the arrangement. They should be able to explain how to use the right-angle checker.

Some children will not have made so much progress and will find it difficult to locate all of the right angles without support. They may not appreciate how the right-angle checker can be used to confirm a right angle. This might result in them placing it randomly in corners of the shapes in the shape arrangements, not taking account of the sides of the shapes to line the checker up against.

Some children will have progressed further and will be able to find all of the right angles, including those in shapes that are not in horizontal-vertical orientations and those that are external to the arrangements. They will be able to articulate what a right angle is and explain how to identify one using a range of appropriate mathematical vocabulary.

Further practice

Children struggling need more opportunities to use a right-angle checker looking for right angles in shapes and in a range of common objects (e.g. table and bookshelf corners).

Evaluation Notes

Year 2 Assessment Task 15

Mass

- **Assessment Foci:** L2 Using and applying (problem solving); L2 Shape, space and measures (measures)
- **Objectives:** ■ Estimate, measure and compare weights using standard units: kilograms, grams ■ Use and begin to read the vocabulary related to length, mass and capacity
- **Suggested Blocks:** C2.a
- **Resources:** 1kg, 500g, 100g, 50g, 20g, 10g, 5g and 1g plastic weights; apples, onions and carrots in different sizes; two identical plastic bags; bucket balances; small balances; round-ended knife; rice or sand; packets with the weights concealed (some big but light; others heavy but small); salt dough

Activity

Show children a kilogram and other gram weights and explain that there are 1000g in a kilogram. Pass the weights round so that children can compare them. Then place some apples in one bag and a kilogram weight in the other. Invite each child to hold a bag in either hand and to say which bag is the heavier. Check using the bucket balance. Then ask children to choose a vegetable. Challenge them to make a bag of their chosen vegetable balance with a kilogram weight.

Observe and ask

- *Which is heavier, the kilogram weight or the 100g weight?*
- *Can you make the vegetables balance with the kilogram? Do both sides balance? What will you need to do to make both sides balance?*
- Do children replace their vegetables with ones of different sizes to help equalise their balance? (e.g. do they replace a large carrot with a small one to reduce the overall weight of their carrots?)
- Observe carefully to see how they adjust the vegetable side to achieve a balance.
- *How do you know that both sides weigh the same?*

Differentiating the task

▼ ***Support:*** In addition to the vegetables, use rice or sand (or just use a food stuff such as rice) in order to make it more likely that children will achieve evenly-balanced scales.

▲ ***Extend:*** Give the group several packages to weigh accurately on the balance scales, using different weights to balance the packages. Then encourage children to line up their packages in order, from the lightest to the heaviest. If appropriate, can they find the diffference in weight?

Expectations

Most children will be able to hold a bag in either hand and say which is the heavier. However, they may find it difficult to achieve a balance. They will need to be patient and systematic as they add and take vegetables out of their bag to match the kilogram weight. Encourage children to explain that they are choosing an apple that is smaller than the one they have taken out and to give reasons. *Smaller apples are lighter than bigger apples.* If after trying with apples they fail to achieve a balance, they may like to try cutting an apple in half. They may have to be satisfied with nearly balancing the scales. Children may like to try using sand. Encourage them to explain why this is easier.

Some children will not have made so much progress and will be able to establish which bag is heavier and which is lighter but will find establishing a balance very difficult. As the vegetable/fruit side becomes heavier, this group of children is likely to begin putting sand in the kilogram weight side to balance the scales – the *wrong* side. Encourage use of the correct language when working, such as *heavier, lighter, heavier than*, *lighter than.*

Some children will have progressed further and will also be able to use the appropriate language correctly and make adjustments easily. They should be able to weigh accurately and systematically, working from the biggest weights to the smallest. They will be able to answer detailed questions, such as: *Do you think your package weighs more or less than a kilogram?* (e.g. *More.*) *Which weight will you begin with to test this?* (e.g. *A kilogram weight.*) *Does it weigh more?* (e.g. *No.*) *What will you try next?* (e.g. *500g.*) This group will be able to order their packages from the lightest to the heaviest, and they may be able to find differences in weight between some objects.

Further practice

Children can use salt dough to make snakes that exactly balance with 20g, 30g etc (up to 1kg). Encourage children to use the correct language when explaining what they are doing. Most children will make the snake first and then attempt to balance it with 20g. Instead, encourage them to balance the lump of dough with the 20g first.

Evaluation Notes

Year 2 Assessment Task 16

Interpreting a block graph

- **Assessment Foci:** L2 Using and applying (communicating); L2 Number (solving numerical problems); L2 Handling data (interpreting data)
- **Objectives:** ■ Sort, organise and interpret information in a block graph
- **Suggested Blocks:** C2.c
- **Resources:** PCM E (one copy per child); whiteboards and pens

Activity

Discuss the general features of a block graph with reference to PCM E, which shows the favourite fruits of a particular class. Go on to discuss what the block graph on PCM E shows. *How does the height of the blocks relate to numbers of children? What is the significance of the height of the block? What does it mean if two blocks are the same?* Ask some further questions in relation to the block graph on PCM E. Some have been outlined on the PCM. Children who are confident should be given time to work through the questions independently, noting the answers on the sheet. (***Note:*** If you ask children to work individually, check first that they understand the vocabulary used on the PCM.) Other children may benefit from having the questions posed verbally and writing answers on a whiteboard, checking through each before continuing. Since this is an assessment of children's interpretation, chose the way of presentation to suit the child.

Observe and ask

- *What does the graph show?*
- *What does the height of the block tell you?*
- *How can you find the difference between the height of two of the blocks?*
- Can children use the graph to elicit the information needed to answer the questions?

Differentiating the task

▼ ***Support:*** Go through each of the fruits marking the number of each at the top of the blocks. Ensure that children refer to these numbers when answering the questions.

▲ ***Extend:*** Ask children to conduct a similar survey of the preferences of the class and draw up a similar graph.

Expectations

Most children will be able to understand the features of a block graph. They will be able to extract the information needed to answer the questions and explain how they are doing so. Some may find the comparison questions trickier to understand than the addition ones, particularly if trying to link them to number sentences. They will find it simpler to count on from the shorter block to the taller block, whichever way around the question is posed.

Some children will not have made so much progress and will find it difficult to extract the information needed to answer the questions without some prompting. They may struggle with the vocabulary involved which will limit their ability to explain how questions can be solved.

Some children will have progressed further and will also give an articulate explanation of the features of the graph. They will answer the questions concisely using a range of appropriate mathematical language to describe what they are doing.

Further practice

Children struggling would benefit from looking at pictograms, which are less abstract. It is also useful to look at block graphs showing the same information as a pictogram in order that children can make the link.

Evaluation Notes

Year 2 Assessment Task 17

3D shapes

- **Assessment Foci:** L2 Using and applying (communicating); L2 Shape, space and measures (properties of shape)
- **Objectives:** ■ Sort 3D shapes and describe their features: number of faces and corners
- **Suggested Blocks:** D2.b
- **Resources:** 3D shapes (pyramid, cuboid, cube, cylinder, cone and sphere); labels marked *pyramid, cuboid, cube, cylinder, cone, sphere*; feely bag; card cut into 2D shapes (square, circular, triangular, rectangular); Polydron; scissors; labels marked *circular, triangular, rectangular, square faces*; scissors; sticky tape

Activity

Give one of each 3D shape to children and display the labels (see **Resources**). Read the labels together and ask each child to say at least two things to describe each of their shapes in turn. Talk about the number of faces/corners/edges/types of face on their shape. If possible, children should find the correct 3D shape label and stick it to the shape. Now place a matching set of 3D shapes into a feely bag. Children take turns to feel a shape in the bag describe it to the group. The group tries to identify the shape by finding the matching shape. Check by matching the shape and the correct label.

Observe and ask

- *How many faces can you see on your shape?*
- Do they count accurately or do they just know?
- *Can you name the faces?*
- *Does your shape have flat or curved faces?*
- *How many corners/edges does it have?*
- *Find the label to match your shape. How do you know it is that shape?*
- Can children describe the shape in the bag?
- Do they need to be prompted to describe the shape?
- Can they describe how many of each face the shape has?

Differentiating the task

▼ ***Support:*** Choose a 3D shape for each child. They identify the faces by sticking the appropriate 2D-shaped pieces of card onto each face of the shape, then sticking the correct 2D shape label to each face. Focus on using the correct vocabulary when working on this activity to avoid confusion of terms.

▲ ***Extend:*** Challenge this group to use Polydron to investigate:

- ☐ how many 3D shapes they can make with six faces;
- ☐ how many different pyramids they can make.

How do you know that the shapes are different? Describe the faces and say how many corners/edges they have. Name the 3D shape.

Expectations

Most children will be able to describe a range of properties of the 3D shapes, including faces, corners and edges. They should be able to identify the 2D shapes that are the faces of the 3D shapes. In most cases they should be able to use these features to identify the correct names for the 3D shapes. ***Note:*** the difference between cubes and cuboids may be tricky at this stage.

Some children will not have made so much progress and will find naming the 3D shapes very difficult. They may be able to identify 2D shapes and be able to label the faces. They will be able to count the number of faces but will find it harder when there is more than one type of face in the 3D shape. The vocabulary *face*, *edges* and *corners* will be difficult for this group to remember and they will confuse corners with edges.

Some children will have progressed further and will also be able to make several different 3D shapes with Polydron. These children will be able to name in advance some of the shapes they will be making. They should be able to name faces and know the number of faces before making the shape. They will probably need to count the edges and corners. They should be encouraged to choose the required Polydron pieces before beginning the model.

Further practice

Ask children to make simple 3D Polydron shapes and to open these out to show the net. Place this net onto card, draw round it, cut it out, fold the edges and join them together with tape. Ask children to draw appropriate 2D-shape faces on each side round the net.

Evaluation Notes

Year 2 Assessment Task 18

Subtracting 10

- **Assessment Foci:** L2 Using and applying (communicating); L2 Number (mental methods)
- **Objectives:** ■ Subtract a multiple of 10 from a 2-digit number by counting back in 10s ■ Add and subtract 9 and 11 by adding and subtracting 10
- **Suggested Blocks:** D2.c; D2.d
- **Resources:** 0–99 number square; L-shaped piece of transparent plastic or acetate (to fit over three numbers on the number square, e.g. 17, 27 and 28); individual whiteboards and pens; 10p and 1p coins; counters; tens and units place-value cards; abacus

Activity

Practice counting in tens on the number square. Point to 97. Ask children how many tens and how many units it has. *If we count back one ten, where will we be? (87) How do you know?* Check, then repeat subtracting ten from other 2-digit numbers. Make sure that children can all explain what will happen when you subtract ten – that the units will stay the same but the tens number will always be one fewer. Then practise subtracting 11 from a 2-digit number, e.g. *29 – 11.* Place the transparent L-shape over the numbers and model taking away ten and one more. Check the strategies that children use (taking away ten then one) before moving on to taking away nine from a 2-digit number. Again, clarify the strategies children use to do this (taking away ten then adding one).

Observe and ask

- *What happens to the tens/units numbers in 97 when we take away ten?*
- *Why does the units number stay the same?*
- *What happens if we take away 11?*
- *Is 11 more or less than ten?*
- *How many tens are there in 11? How many units?*
- Do children say the answer?
- (For 65–11) Can children write the answer immediately? (Do they use the number square for reference?)

Differentiating the task

▼ ***Support:*** Use a number square and give each child 10p and 1p coins. Place a counter on 53 and make 53p with 10p and 1p coins. Ask children to take away 10p. *How much is left?* (*43p*) *Where should I move the counter to show 53 – 10 on the number square?* Repeat a few times before working with this group to take away 11, modelling the strategy using 10p and 1p coins.

▲ ***Extend:*** Use tens and units place-value cards to add and subtract 9 and 11. Extend to adding or subtracting 19, 21, 18, 22 and near multiples of ten.

Expectations

Most of the children will be able to take away 10 from any 2-digit number. Most will also be able to add and take away 11 and 9 and understand this as a two-step operation, i.e. taking away 10 then adjusting. They should be able to discuss and explain their strategies. Some may find explaining the strategy for 9 trickier (since it involves subtraction and addition).

Some children will not have made so much progress and will need to make the 2-digit numbers with 10p and 1p coins and relate these to the number square. When subtracting ten, they can demonstrate that the tens number reduces by one but the units number remains the same. They will still find difficulty reducing numbers in the twenties by ten. These children often resort to counting ten back in ones when they are asked to subtract ten from a number. Because they are counting back, they are also more likely to miscount and make errors. These children are very likely to adjust the 'wrong way' when subtracting 11 (i.e. by adding one instead of subtracting one).

Some children will have progressed further and will also be able to add and subtract 9 and 11. Many will be also able to take away or add 19, 21, 18, 22 and near multiples of ten. They will be able to use place-value cards to demonstrate their understanding. Bridging over ten may need extra practice. This group may make an error in the manipulation of cards to show their calculation. For example: $29 + 21 = 29 + 20 + 1 = 49 + 1 = 40$ (i.e. changing the nine to a zero but forgetting to alter then tens digit accordingly).

Further practice

Choose a 2-digit number on the 0–99 number square and place a counter on that number. *How will you make the number with the place-value cards? Is your number the same as the number on the square? Use your place-value cards to take away ten. What is your new number? How many tens/units does it have?* If children are hesitant, use 10p and 1p coins or an abacus to consolidate.

Evaluation Notes

Year 2 Assessment Task 19

Division as the inverse of multiplication

- **Assessment Foci:** L2 Number (mental methods; solving numerical problems)
- **Objectives:** ■ Record multiplication facts using × and = in number sentences ■ Introduce division as the inverse of multiplication
- **Suggested Blocks:** E2.c; E2.d
- **Resources:** 1–100 number square; 10p, 5p and 1p coins; number fans; individual whiteboards and pens; cylindrical crisp container with a slit in the lid; interlocking cubes

Activity

Rehearse counting in twos, fives and tens, matching the count with fingers and on the number square. You could also show the calculations using 2p, 5p and 10p coins. Give out number fans and ask questions so children can show answers, e.g. *5 × 2, 6 × 2, 5 × 5, 6 × 5, 10 × 5* and *9 × 5*. Prompt the group with questions. *If five lots of two equals ten, what will four lots of two be? Eight (or one lot of two less than ten).* Model this with coins. *Can you use this strategy to find six times two? Nine times two? Eleven times two?* Remind children that multiplication is repeated addition and ask them to write each number sentence using the × symbol. Then work on some inverse division calculations, e.g. *What is five times ten? (Five lots of 10p?) So how many 10p pieces are in 50p?* Model the sum with coins and the number square.

Observe and ask

- *Count in twos with your fingers. What is two times two?*
- *Who can show the counting in twos pattern on the number square? With coins?*
- *What are four lots of 2p? Show me the answer using the fans. What strategy did you use?*
- Did children use fingers and count from one lot of two? Did they quickly show 5 × 2 with fingers and take away two? Did they just know?
- *Can you write the multiplication number sentence?*
- *How many 2p coins are in 6p?*

Differentiating the task

▼ ***Support:*** Place six 2p coins on the table. *How much money is that? How many 2p coins are there?* Model the answer, asking for children's help. *How many coins do we have? What kind of coins are they? How much money is that altogether?* Match this to six lots of 2p = 12p. *Who can write the addition number sentence? Is the answer the same?*

▲ ***Extend:*** Tell children you will be dropping some coins into a container. Ask them to keep a tally with their fingers as the coins are dropped in, and then to write the multiplication and division number sentences. For example, drop four 5p coins in a pot and ask children to write the number sentence *(4 × 5p = 20p)* and then read it *(four lots of 5p equals 20p)*. They then write and read the corresponding division number sentence *(20p ÷ 5p = 4, 20p divided into 5p coins is four coins.)*

Expectations

Most children will be able to count in twos, fives and tens using fingers. They should know ×5 and ×10 for two, five and ten. They should be able to work out near multiples, e.g. *(4 × 2, 6 × 2, 9 × 2* and *11 × 2)* using the strategies practised in the activity that are essential for quick calculation. Most will be able to divide by two and ten for familiar multiples and recognise the relationship between the two operations.

Some children will not have made so much progress and will still be struggling with basic multiplication facts. They should all be able to count 2p, 5p and 10p coins (3 × 5 may be difficult) and solve some multiplication questions using repeated addition. They will not make the connection between multiplication and division. Some may also confuse the symbols for multiplication and addition.

Some children will have progressed further and will also be able to write the multiplication and division number sentences for each problem. They will be able to use the division symbol when writing their number sentences and to read their sentences.

Further practice

Use interlocking cubes to make sets of two, five or ten. Encourage children to count these quickly. Give each child a number square. *Can you remember the counting in twos pattern? How can you count in twos on the number square?* Place three two-cube towers on the table. *How many groups are there? How many in each group? How many altogether? Show me how to write three lots of two equals six as an addition (2 + 2 + 2 = 6).* If appropriate, go on to say that we can write this in a shorter way, using the '×' symbol to mean *lots of*, e.g. *3 × 2 = 6.*

Evaluation Notes

Year 2 Assessment Task 20 — Place value

- **Assessment Foci:** L2^{+} Number (numbers and number system)
- **Objectives:** ■ Read and write numbers up to 100 in figures ■ Begin to partition 3-digit numbers into H, T and U
- **Suggested Blocks:** A3.a
- **Resources:** 0–99 number square; individual whiteboards and pens; Post-It Notes; hundreds, tens and units place-value cards; Multibase apparatus (flats, longs and units); 0–9 number cards

Activity

Pin up the number square and point to a number, e.g. *47. How many tens are there? How many units?* Repeat for 99. *Which number comes next? Write the number.* Check children's answers. Write *100* on a Post-It Note and place it on zero on the number square. Ask children to add a hundred to numbers on the number square. Repeat up to an appropriate number, such as 124. Then give children the hundreds, tens and units place-value cards and ask them to make 3-digit numbers.

Observe and ask

- *Look at 25. How many tens does it have? How many units?*
- *Who can write 125?*
- *How is it different from 25?*
- *Is there an extra digit? What do you think this new digit could be?* (A hundred)
- *How much bigger than 47 is 147? How do you know?*
- *Can you show me how to make 367 using your place-value cards? How did you make this number? In what order did you gather your cards?*
- *Now make the number one bigger. Which digit will you change? Why? Which digits stay the same? Why?*
- *How will you make the number 100 bigger?*

Differentiating the task

▼ ***Support:*** On the board, write a 2-digit number and ask children to make it using Multibase equipment and place-value cards. *How will you make 47 with tens and units? How many longs (tens) do you need? How many ones? How would you make the number with place-value cards? Can you make the number one/ten bigger/smaller?*

▲ ***Extend:*** Use both place-value cards and Multibase apparatus to make 3-digit numbers. Then ask children to make these numbers larger or smaller by 2- or 3-digit numbers of increasing difficulty, by changing the appropriate digits.

Expectations

Most children will be able to read and write 3-digit numbers. However, some may find the numbers from 100 to 120 difficult to write. From 100 to 109, the tens zero place holder can be difficult to understand, and children will sometimes write 100 and 1 as 1001, 100 and 2 as 1002 etc. From 110 to 119 the teen numbers add a further complication. Children will see how the 100 changes the 2-digit number and realise that the tens and units stay the same. Clarify this by asking children to write different hundred numbers, asking where they should be placed and giving reasons. When using the place-value cards, reinforce that children should find the hundreds number first, then the tens and finally the units.

Some children will not have made so much progress and will still be finding 2-digit numbers difficult. Check that they can make all 2-digit numbers with Multibase and place-value cards. In addition, they need to be confident increasing or decreasing 2-digit numbers by 1 and 10. However, they need to see a 3-digit number square and see the similarities/differences between 2- and 3-digit numbers.

Some children will have progressed further and will also be able to use place-value cards and Multibase apparatus to make 3-digit numbers. They will confidently increase/decrease any 3-digit number by 100, 10 or 1. Some will also be able to increase/decrease by all three digits e.g. making 342, 134 bigger, which is indicative of L3 in this Assessment Focus. Bridging over tens or hundreds may be difficult, with some children neglecting to adjust all digits in their haste to make the new number. To rectify any mistakes, they should be encouraged first to work mentally and jot down the answer, then check with place-value cards. With some calculations, it is easier to work out the answer before using the place-value cards.

Further practice

Make a 3-digit number square to practise counting in ones and tens. Use Multibase and place-value cards to consolidate children's understanding of numbers 100 to 199. Discuss how the other hundred numbers would be written.

Evaluation Notes

Year 2 Assessment Task 21

Fractions

- **Assessment Foci:** L2 Number (fractions)
- **Objectives:** ■ Begin to recognise halves and quarters of small numbers of objects ■ Recognise fraction notation
- **Suggested Blocks:** B3.b
- **Resources:** paper circles (to represent cakes); red counters (to represent cherries); paper squares and rectangles; individual whiteboards and pens

Activity

Ask each child to fold a paper circle in half, checking that the edges fit exactly. Explain that the whole circle (or cake) has been divided in half. Write *half* on the board and ask the children to write *half* on one side of the folded paper circle. *How many halves are there in the whole circle?* (*two*) Write $\frac{1}{2}$ on the board and explain the notation. Hold up the semicircle to indicate half the cake, then open the circle to show two halves. *There are two halves in a whole cake. Take six red counters (cherries) and share them so that both halves of your cake have the same number of cherries.* Repeat for other even numbers up to 20 cherries. Then repeat the activity, but this time for quarters using 12 cherries only, folding the 'cake' in half twice.

Observe and ask

- Do children all fold the paper exactly in half?
- Do they all understand the fraction notation $\frac{1}{2}$?
- *How many halves are there in the whole cake? Can you show me half of the cake?*
- *Share 12 cherries so that each cake half has the same number. How many cherries on each half of the cake? How many on the whole cake?*
- Can children write *half of 12 is…* on their whiteboard?
- *How many quarters make half? Are two quarters the same as one half?*

Differentiating the task

▼ ***Support:*** Repeat the activity for halving up to 12 cherries but do not introduce quartering of numbers, only quartering of shapes. Use circles, squares and rectangles to demonstrate this.

▲ ***Extend:*** Work on halving bigger numbers with this group, for example: *What is half of 42? 36? 48? How did you work out half of 36?* Extend the work on quarters up to 24 cherries.

Expectations

Most children will be able to halve the paper, although some may need help with putting the edges exactly together. They should understand the relationship between two halves and a whole. They should be able to recognise and write simple fractions (e.g. $\frac{1}{2}$, $\frac{1}{4}$) using appropriate notation. They should be able to answer questions about how many cherries are on each half and the whole cake and be able to share the cherries between the four quarters when the number given is a multiple of 4 (e.g. 12, 16 or 20).

Some children will not have made so much progress and will find it difficult to make connections between different models of fractions. They will find quarters significantly harder to understand then halves. The notation of fractions will also be problematic.

Some children will have progressed further and will also be able to work out half of bigger numbers by halving the tens and halving the units and then adding these together. Halving numbers in the thirties, fifties, seventies and nineties are more difficult. One likely strategy children will use is to split the number into two or more easily halved sections, halve those, then add them together. E.g. to find half of 36, a child might find half of 30 and half of six (or half of 20, half of 10 and half of 6), and add them together. This group should be making the association between doubling and halving. Quartering needs to be kept below 24, using numbers that can be physically divided.

Further practice

Use fingers to halve and double up to *5 + 5* by showing thumbs together: *one and one make two, half of two is one*, etc. Use toes to extend to adding 10 + 10. *Five toes and one thumb and five toes and one thumb is 6 + 6, and 6 + 6 is 12. Half of 12 is six.* Repeat up to 10 + 10.

Evaluation Notes

Year 2 Assessment Task 22

Reading scales

- **Assessment Foci:** L2 Shape, space and measures (measures)
- **Objectives:** ■ Begin to read a simple capacity scale to the nearest labelled and unlabelled division
- **Suggested Blocks:** C3.a
- **Resources:** litre bottle; jug of water; sticky labels; individual whiteboards and pens; yoghurt pot; funnel

Activity

Draw a large jug on the board and write that there are 1000ml in one litre. Read this with the class and explain that you are going to draw on a scale (using sticky labels) to show millilitres. *Do you think we can fit in 1000 division lines onto our jug? Why/why not?* Explain that you are going to draw equal divisions but will need help with labelling them. Divide the jug into hundreds. *Help me to label my divisions.* Label alternate divisions (*200ml, 400ml… 1000ml*), explaining that the numbers would be too small to read if they were all written onto the jug. Draw some water in the jug. *How much water have I poured in? Who can read the scale?*

Observe and ask

- *If I was asked to put a litre of water into the jug, where would the level be?*
- *How many millilitres would that be?*
- *Can you write down how many millilitres there would be if I filled the jug to this mark? How do you know? How did you work it out?*
- Can children work out answers for other calibrated but unlabelled divisions?
- *If I half-filled the jug how much water would there be? How do you know?*
- Do they immediately point to the halfway mark between 400ml and 600ml?
- (Point to an imaginary halfway division between 200ml and 300ml.) *If I filled to this imaginary division, how much water would there be?*

Differentiating the task

▼ ***Support:*** Draw a jug to hold 100ml and demarcate it into 10ml, labelling *0, 20, 40, 60, 80* and *100ml*. Ask similar questions to those for the core group, focussing on the marked but unlabelled divisions. When children are confident with solving the problem with this smaller scale attempt the original problem again.

▲ ***Extend:*** For this group calibrate the jug into hundreds with lines, the fifties with dots and label *0, 500* and *1000ml,* so that 0, 500 and 1000 are the only numbers on the scale. Ask questions about multiples of 50, and questions that relate 250, 500 and 750ml to quarter, half and three-quarters of a litre.

Expectations

Most children will be able to use the scale to find the in-between numbers, but some may need to count in hundreds from zero to work this out. You may need to be more specific than pointing to the division and say: *How many millilitres to this mark between 200ml and 400ml?* It is important that children can all find or know how many millilitres are in half a litre. They should all know that half of 1000 is 500, and should be able to relate this to half of 100 and half of ten. However, additional teaching will be needed for quarter and three-quarters.

Some children will not have made so much progress and will find it difficult to use the demarcations on the 0–1000ml jug. Using the demarcations on the 0–100ml jug may serve as a prompt.

Some children will have progressed further and will also be able to find all demarcations on a 0–1000ml jug. Encourage these children to say *half a litre*, *quarter of a litre* and *three-quarters of a litre*. This group is unlikely to make counting errors, although they are likely to count from zero, e.g. *0, 100, 200, 300, 350* to read 350ml.

Further practice

Use yoghurt pots and a litre bottle. Each time a yoghurt pot is emptied into the litre bottle, ask children to mark the level with a sticky label. *How many pots did the bottle hold? Write the numbers of yoghurt pots on two of the labels. Which two will you choose? Why don't we need all the strips labelled? Can you fill the bottle up to three yoghurt pots-full? How? Will you need yoghurt pots? Why/why not? How did you know without all the numbers being labelled?* Ask children to imagine that each yoghurt pot holds ten thimbles. Can they recalibrate the container accordingly?

Evaluation Notes

Year 2 Assessment Task 23

Missing numbers

- **Assessment Foci:** L2 Number (operations, relationships; mental methods; written methods)
- **Objective:** ■ Understand that subtraction is the inverse of addition, using missing number sentences
- **Suggested Blocks:** D3.b
- **Resources:** individual whiteboards and pens; cubes; 8–14 number cards; two plates for each child; Post-It Notes; 1–6 dice

Activity

Write a number sentence on the board, such as *30 + □ = 100* and ask children to read the sentence out, e.g. *30 add something equals 100* or *30 and how many more make 100*. Discuss strategies for solving the problem. Now write on the board *100 – □ = 30* and read the number sentence as *100 take away something equals 30*. Discuss children's strategies for solving this. Then write these problems for children to work out: *□ + 20 = 90, 20 + □ = 80, 50 – □ = 5* and *70 – □ = 50*.

Observe and ask

- *How can we find out what to put in the square?*
- Do children count on with fingers up to 100?
- Do they hold up ten fingers (each digit representing ten) and fold down three (30)?
- Do they hold 100 in their head and count back 30?
- *How can we solve the subtraction problem?*
- Do they put 100 in their head and count back 30?
- Do they put 30 in their head and count on to 100?
- Do they hold up ten fingers (100) and fold down three (30)?
- *Complete these number sentences on your whiteboards. Which problem was the easiest/most difficult? Why?*

Differentiating the task

▼ ***Support:*** Use much smaller numbers. This is an opportunity to consolidate number bonds for 10 and 20. Write on the board *7 + □ = 10* and read this as *seven and some more make ten*. Encourage children to show ten with the fingers and fold down three fingers, or to count on from seven. Then give them the following problems to solve: *17 + □ = 20,10 – □ = 7* and *20 – □ = 17*.

▲ ***Extend:*** Use more difficult addition and subtraction problems which involve multiples of ten, e.g. *43 + □ = 83, 94 – □ = 54, 96 + □ = 126* and *87 – □ = 27*. Also try some with two missing numbers. *Write two different calculations for these problems: □ + □ = 38* and *□ – □ = 54*.

Expectations

Most children will be able to solve the missing number problems by using number bond knowledge (e.g. *since 3 + 7 = 10, 30 + 70 = 100*). They should also make the connection between addition and subtraction sentences (e.g. *since 30 + 70 = 100, 100 – 70 = 30*). Children need to know that in addition the numbers can be written in any order, but that in subtraction the larger number is always written first and the amount taken away second.

Some children will not have made so much progress and will find the empty boxes confusing. They are likely to have a poor understanding of the relationship between addition and subtraction which makes it difficult for them to solve the problems in a strategic way. Prompted by physical resources such as cubes they may solve some of the questions.

Some children will have progressed further and will also be able to find the missing numbers using a variety of different strategies. Finding two missing numbers will give you opportunities for discussing the many different answers available.

Further practice

In order to gain their confidence, try giving children some very easy addition problems with two missing numbers. Give each child a number card between 8 and 14. They collect that number of cubes and arrange them on two plates. They then write the addition number sentence, e.g. *5 + 9 = 14*. How many different sentences can they write? If these are written on separate Post-It Notes, they can be arranged in order. To explain subtraction, hand each child a number card, e.g. 12. The child throws a 1–6 dice and takes that number of cubes away, e.g. *12 – 6 = 6*.

Evaluation Notes

Year 2 Assessment Task 24

Multiples of 2, 5 and 10

- **Assessment Foci:** L2 Number (mental methods)
- **Objectives:** ■ Recognise 2-digit multiples of 2, 5 and 10, and know their multiplication facts
- **Suggested Blocks:** E3.b
- **Resources:** 1–100 square; 10-point counting stick; 2p, 5p and 10p coins

Activity

Rehearse counting in twos using the 10-point counting stick with ends of 0 and 20. Stress the mid-point, i.e. 10. Choose children to write the multiples of 2, in sequence and discuss the patterns in the digits. Repeat this process for multiples of 10, and of 5.

Observe and ask

- Start with multiples of 2 and point along the counting stick in ascending sequence. *Where am I pointing?*
- Point along the counting stick in descending sequence. *Where am I pointing?*
- Now point at different positions randomly, e.g. at 6 × 2. *Where am I pointing?* Emphasise that this position is the sixth multiple. *Six twos are twelve.* Write *6 × 2 = 12.*
- Repeat the process for multiples of 10 and of 5.

Differentiating the task

▼ ***Support:*** Use a 1–100 square and invite children to colour the multiples of 2 up to 20, in one colour, then multiples of 5 up to 50 in another. Ask multiplication facts, e.g. *7 × 2*. Children can count along the square in twos. Make a link between this and the counting stick.

▲ ***Extend:*** Use number cards 1 to 20, 25, 30, 35, 40, 45 and 50. Shuffle them and reveal them one at a time. For each number: *Is it a multiple of 10? 5? 2?* If the answer is *Yes* to any of these questions, challenge children to write a number sentence, e.g. for card 18, write *9 × 2 = 18*. Use this activity to discuss how some numbers, e.g. 10 are multiples of 2, of 5 and of 10.
These children can also be given over 50 cubes to count. Ask them to count the cubes in groups of two. More able children in this group will count *2, 4, 6…* Some may be able to count the cubes into groups of ten and then count *10, 20…* etc.

Expectations

Most children will be able to count in twos, fives and tens, and be able to respond to questions (e.g. *What are six twos?*) by counting along their fingers. Children should be able to recognise, having experienced using the counting stick, that six twos are the next multiple of 2 after 10 or five twos, i.e. the mid-point of the stick, and therefore not need to count twos in sequence from 0. Most children will also be able to begin to write number sentences relating to this, e.g. *6 × 2 = 12.*

Some children will not have made so much progress and will not necessarily recognise and use patterns in the sequences to support counting in multiples. They may know the isolated multiplication fact (e.g. 2 × 5) but not generally make the connection between counting in multiples and to establishing multiplication facts.

Some children will have progressed further and will also be able to write number sentences for ×2, ×5 and ×10. They will also recognise multiples of 2, 5 and 10 beyond the tenth multiple. They will also begin to understand the inverse, e.g. *How many fives make forty?* and record it (e.g. *40 ÷ 5 = 8*).

Further practice

Use a pile of ten 2p coins, a pile of ten 5p coins and a pile of ten 10p coins. Choose a child to take some coins from one of the piles, and count how many coins, e.g., from the pile of 5p coins – *How many coins?* Seven. *How much money? Seven fives are thirty five pence*. Choose a child to record this, i.e. *7 × 5 = 35*. Replace the coins and repeat, choosing different children at each stage.

Evaluation Notes

Year 2 Assessment Task 25

Strategies for doubling and halving

- **Assessment Foci:** L2 Number (operations, relationships; mental methods)
- **Objectives:** ■ Double multiples of 5 up to 50 ■ Begin to halve multiples of 10 up to 100
- **Suggested Blocks:** E3.c
- **Resources:** 5p and 10p coins; cloth; individual whiteboards and pens

Activity

Place two 5p coins slightly apart on the table and ask children to say *5p + 5p = 10p* and *double 5p is 10p*. Write *double 5p =10p* and *5p + 5p = 10p* on the board, then ask: *What is half of 10p?* Now put two 10p coins on the table, slightly apart and ask: *What is double 10p? How would you write that as a number sentence? What is half of 10p?* Write $\frac{1}{2}$ *of 10p = 5p* on the board. Give each child 5p and 10p coins and repeat the activity, this time with them modelling the calculations you give, e.g. doubles of 25p, 35p and 45p.

Observe and ask

- *Can you show me double 15?*
- Do they count out two sets of 15p?
- Do they write down the answer immediately?
- Do they count on from 15p?
- Do they count in fives from the beginning?
- *Can you write the answer for half of 20p?*
- *How about double/half of 50/100?*

Differentiating the task

▼ ***Support:*** Use 10p coins to revise doubling multiples of ten. Introduce halving as the inverse by saying: *If double 10p equals 20p, what is half 20p?* It may help to place a cloth over half the amount to reinforce the halving. Practise doubling tens up to 100, but only halve 100, 80, 60, 40, 20 and 10. When you feel it is appropriate, use 5p coins to double multiples of five up to 20. Encourage each child to use coins and to work out the answer. Once it has been worked out help them to memorise by writing down the number sentence. *Can you see any patterns?*

▲ ***Extend:*** This group can double and halve bigger numbers, if you are systematic with your questioning. For example: *What is double 45?* Double the tens first: *40 + 40 = 80*, then double the units: *5 + 5 = 10*, and now add them together: *8 + 10 = 90*. To halve multiples of ten, help children follow this method.
For example: *What is half of 90? Find half of 100* (*50*). *Then find half of 80* (*40*). *So half of 90 is 45.*

Expectations

Most children will be able to double multiples of five but some may find doubles of 15p, 25p, 35p and 45p more difficult. Halving 10p, 20p, 40p, 60p, 80p and 100p should not be a problem and, with coins, children should be able to solve the problem of halving 30, 50, 70 or 90.

Some children will not have made so much progress and will be unable to double multiples of ten confidently. They will only have a weak grasp of the relationship between doubling and halving and may have difficulty using the correct mathematical vocabulary to describe what they are doing. Halving 30, 50, 70 and 90 will be most difficult for these children.

Some children will have progressed further and will also be able to find the answers to more complex halving and doubling questions. Bigger numbers will need a more systematic approach. Try to elicit as many different strategies as possible. It is possible that some children may use their knowledge that double 50 is 100 and adjust.

Further practice

Children use fingers to double and halve multiples of ten to 100. They place thumbs together, saying: *Ten plus ten equals 20*; pull them apart saying: *Half of 20 is ten.* Repeat up to *50 + 50 = 100* and *half of 100 is 50.*

Evaluation Notes

Y2 Review of pre-requisite skills for Block A1.a and A1.b

Objectives:

- Say numbers in order up to 50 and back
- Recognise figures 1–30 and match to the spoken number
- Match numbers 1–20 to a quantity

Mental oral starter:

Finger-matching numbers

Children work with a partner. They put their hands behind their back, say a number between 11 and 20, then hold their hands up, showing that many fingers between them – they must work out how best to do this. Stress there are many ways. Choose different children to be the 'teller' – the person who says the number. The rest of the class show a matching number of fingers as fast as possible.

Teaching sequence:

- With children, count up to ten, matching each number spoken to the number of fingers. Wave both hands to stress ten is all our fingers. Continue to 20, then on to 50. With each multiple of five, children wave a hand or both hands (for multiples of ten).
- Show children a large 1–30 number line. Hand out number cards, 1–30, one card per child. Tell them to keep their number hidden.
- Ask one child to stand but NOT show others their number.
- Model questions children can ask to help guess the number. *Is your number more than 20?* If 'no', cover/remove numbers it cannot be, for example, those more than 20.
- Choose another child to ask a question, for example, *Is it less than ten?* Cover/remove numbers it cannot be.
- Encourage different types of question: *Is it even? Has it got a '3' in it?*
- When children think they know, they guess.
- Repeat the process for several children's card numbers.
- Ask all children holding a card with '3' in it to stand and say the numbers. Repeat for a card with '4' in it, then with '2' in it, then with '1' in it.

Activities:

Independent task: Give children a set of 1–30 number cards. Working in pairs, they order them on a 3 × 10 grid, then work together to build a tower of cubes or thread a line of beads to match three of the numbers.

Teacher-monitored task: Meanwhile, sit with a group of six children at a table, with 10–30 number cards. Each child takes three cards, you have three cards. Explain we start with '10'. The child holding '10' places the card on the table. *What number comes next?* The child holding '11' places the card next to '10' to make a line. Keep asking and continue the line. Encourage children to concentrate so they don't miss their turn. Repeat, counting back from 30 to 10.

Assessment criteria:

- Can say numbers in order to at least 50
- Can match a number 1–20 to a quantity
- Can match spoken numbers 1–30 to written figures
- Can place numbers 1–30 in order along a number line

Plenary:

Write a 'teen' number on board, for example, *13*. Ask children to reverse the digits and tell their partner the number, for example, *31*. Repeat for a different teen number. Ask pairs to write a number that, when the digits are reversed, gives a teen number.

Y2 Review of pre-requisite skills for Block A1.c and A1.d

Objectives:

- Estimate a quantity up to 30
- Place any three numbers up to 30 in order
- Given any two numbers up to 30, find the number in-between

Mental oral starter:

Counting the cubes

Show children a bag with about 28 multilink cubes in it. Ask children to discuss with their partner how many cubes there are, agree an estimate and write it on a whiteboard. Check their estimates. *What is the lowest guess? What is the highest?* Tip the cubes out and count, grouping in fives. *How many? Whose estimate was closest?*

Teaching sequence:

- Show children a 1–30 number grid, arranged in 3 rows of 10 columns. Choose a child to say a number on the grid, for example, *twenty-six*. Write it on the board, *26*.
- Repeat with two other children. Write each number on the board: for example, *30, 12.*
- Look at the numbers on the board: for example, *26, 30, 12. Which is the largest?* Match the numbers to the grid, pointing out that the numbers get larger as we go down the grid, and along each row from left to right. Use the grid to help demonstrate which number is largest.
- Look again at the numbers on the board. *Which is the smallest?* Again, use the grid, pointing out that the numbers get smaller as we go up the grid, and on the left hand side of each row. Use the grid to help demonstrate which number is the smallest.
- Identify the smallest and largest number on the board. *Which number is in the middle?* Place the three numbers in order from smallest to largest.
- Repeat for three new numbers.
- Write two numbers on the board and read, for example, *24* and *18*. Ask children which is larger and which smaller. Put them in order.
- Identify these numbers on the grid. Can children say a number in-between these two? Use the grid to help, for example, *20 comes between 18 and 24*. Repeat with two new numbers.

Activities:

Independent task: Give children PCM R1. Each child works with a partner but completes their own sheet.

Teacher-monitored task: Meanwhile, sit with a group of six children at a table, with number cards 1–30 and one red and one blue mat. Each child takes a pair of cards. In turn, each turns their cards face up, placing the larger one on the red mat, the smaller on the blue mat. The others check that they agree. Each child must say a number between their two numbers. Repeat this at least six times.

Assessment criteria:

- Can order any given three numbers up to 30
- Can say a number between any two numbers up to 30
- Can estimate a quantity up to 30

Plenary:

Show children a tower of 25 multilink cubes for two seconds. Can children estimate how many cubes? They write their estimate on their whiteboard. *Who is closest?*

Y2 Review of pre-requisite skills for Block B1.a and B1.b

Objectives:

- Add 1-digit number to number up to 20 by counting on from larger of two
- Understand that, if we add 0, the number stays the same

Mental oral starter:

Add three

In pairs, children write three numbers from 10 to 18 on their whiteboards and draw a circle round each. Take a card from the set numbered 5–15. *We will add three to this number.* Encourage children to count on from the card number. If any pair has this answer on their whiteboard, they cross it out. Keep playing until one pair has crossed off all the numbers. Bingo! They win.

Teaching sequence:

- Give each child a tower of 1, 2, 3, 4 or 5 cubes. Leave one or two 'special' children with none.
- Write *12* on the board. Ask children to read this aloud. *Twelve*. Show children a 12-cube tower. *This is twelve cubes.*
- Choose a child. *We are going to add your tower of cubes to my tower.* Ask the child how many cubes they have, for example, 3, then write the addition: *12 + 3 =* □.
- *How many cubes do we have in all?* Discuss with the class. Point at two towers. *It is easier to add the small tower to the large one and count on.* Ask the child with the small tower to add his/her cubes one by one to your tower. As s/he does so, count on from twelve together. *Twelve, thirteen, fourteen, fifteen. We now have fifteen cubes.* Complete the addition: *12 + 3 = 15.*
- Repeat with a tower of 14, adding 4.
- Show several sums where we add one of the children's towers to a teen number.
- *What happens if we add 0?* Discuss with the class. Write the addition: *13 + 0 =* □. Point out that we are adding no cubes. *The tower stays the same.*
- Collect all the towers, counting on as you add each to make one massive tower.

Activities:

Independent task: Give each child a copy of PCM 7. They work in pairs, but each child completes their own sheet.

Teacher-monitored task: Sit with a group of eight children at a table, with a set of 10–20 number cards. The children work in pairs, each with a 1–25 number line in front of them. Each pair takes a card and adds four to it, recording the addition, for example, *13 + 4 = 17.* Encourage the children to use their number line if appropriate. Ask each pair to read their addition aloud. *Are they all correct?* Replace the cards and repeat, seven times.

Assessment criteria:

- Can add a 1-digit number to a number up to 20
- Understands that, if 0 is added to a number, the number stays the same.

Plenary:

Write *21* on the board. Ask children to write an addition on their whiteboard where the answer is 21.

Y2 Review of pre-requisite skills for Block B1.c and B1.d

Objectives:

- Recognise pairs of numbers that make 4, 5, and 6
- Add two numbers below 6

Mental oral starter:

Counting the dots

Children take a domino each. In pairs, children find out how many dots they have between them. Count from 1 to 20, asking each pair to stand up as you say their number. Ask children to swap dominoes and repeat.

Teaching sequence:

- Show children two large dice. Explain that you are going to throw the dice and add the totals. If the total is 5, the boys get a team point; if the total is 6, girls get a team point. If the total is 4 or 3, the teacher gets a point!
- Ask the boys to work in pairs to find out how two dice could land so that the total is 5.
- Ask the girls to work in pairs to find out how two dice could land so that the total is 6.
- Take feedback. Record all the possible ways that the boys' dice can land: *1 + 4, 2 + 3, 3 + 2, 4 + 1.*
- Take feedback. Record all the possible ways that the girls' dice can land: *1 + 5, 2 + 4, 3 + 3, 4 + 2* and *5 + 1.*
- *Is this fair?* Discuss. Hopefully one boy will say it is not. Suggest that if the total of the dice is 2, the boys get a team point.
- Discuss all the possible ways the teacher's dice can land: *1 + 3, 2 + 2, 3 + 1* (all make 4) and *1 + 2* and *2 + 1* (both make 3). Point out that this is five ways – the same as for the girls.
- Play on, throwing the dice ten times. Who wins?
- Repeat the game. Who wins this time?

Activities:

Independent task: Give out PCM R2. Children work in pairs, each with their own sheet. They discuss which pair of numbers to colour first, then proceed together until they have both coloured all the numbers.

Teacher-monitored task: In a group of 8–10 children each pair has a set of traditional dominoes. Pairs work to make a line of dominoes where the touching halves total 6, for example, 4/5 next to 1/6 next to 0/3 next to 3/5, etc. Encourage children to recognise the number of dots on each domino half without counting the dots.

Assessment criteria:

- Recognise pairs of numbers that make 5
- Recognise pairs of numbers that make 6

Plenary:

Draw the dice arrangement of six dots. Discuss how we might arrange nine dots. Let children use their whiteboards to try. *What about twelve dots?*

Y2 Review of pre-requisite skills for Block C1.a and C1.b

Objectives:

- Use and understand vocabulary of length, for example 'longer', 'shorter', 'taller'
- Measure length of object using uniform non-standard units
- Compare lengths using uniform non-standard units

Mental oral starter:

Teddy taller

Show the children a teddy bear. *How many multilink cubes tall do we think teddy is?* Encourage children to estimate with a partner. They write their guess on the whiteboard. Build a cube tower the same height as the teddy. Choose some children to help. *How many cubes tall is the teddy? Whose estimate was the closest?*

Teaching sequence:

- Choose a sensible child to stand on a low chair at the front.
- Show the class a straw. *How many straws will we have to put end to end to make Sam's height? How many straws tall is Sam?*
- Use straws to measure the child's height. Fasten with Blu-tac, until you have a 'tower' as near as possible to the same height as the child. Count the straws together.
- Write the measurement on the board: *Sam is 8 straws tall.*
- Ask Sam to stretch out an arm. Show the class a wax crayon. *How many crayons long is Sam's arm?* Children work with a talking partner to estimate.
- Lay a piece of string from Sam's shoulder to fingertips. Cut the string to the right length, demonstrating that the string is now the same length as Sam's arm.
- Lay the string along a table where the class can see. Lay crayons along the length, counting as you go. *How many crayons long is Sam's arm?* Record the length on the board: *Sam's arm is 9 crayons long. Whose estimate was the closest?*
- Compare the length of a different child's arm. Measure with the string, then the crayons. *Is it shorter or longer than Sam's?*
- Discuss the fact that we can use crayons, straws and multilink to measure the length of something. The things we use must all be the same size. Show each straw is the same length.

Activities:

Paired activity for the whole class: Give each pair of children a soft toy to measure. Pairs write an estimate of how many cubes long they think their toy is, then use the cubes to measure the length. Each pair records the length, for example, *Teddy is 15 cubes long*. Compare results. *Whose toy is the longest? Whose is the shortest? Whose is in the middle?* Extend by asking how many cubes longer one toy is than another.

Assessment criteria:

- Understand and use terms 'longer', 'shorter', 'taller' appropriately
- Can use non-standard measure to find length and height of larger objects
- Can compare lengths using non-standard measures

Plenary:

Show the class a book that is almost square. *Which side of the book is longer?* Measure each side with cubes to find out.

Y2 Review of pre-requisite skills for Block C1.c and C1.d

Objectives:

- Use and understand vocabulary related to time
- Recognise names of days of week, months of year and seasons.

Mental oral starter:

Day or month?

Write *Monday, January, Winter, Friday, July, Summer, Saturday, December* on the board. Draw a circle round each. Read each aloud with children, pointing as you read. Tell children some of these are days of the week, some months of the year, some seasons. Ask children with a partner to identify each as day, month, or season. Give them a few minutes, take their feedback then identify each one.

Teaching sequence:

- Sing the song of days of the week, or say the rhyme: *Monday – washing day, Tuesday – clothes all dry, Wednesday – hot soup, Thursday – shepherd's pie, Friday – fish, Saturday – I like best, Sunday – Have a rest!*
- Point out that a week is seven days. *From this day,* for example, Monday, *through the week, past the weekend when we are not at school, to the same day next week is seven days.* Ask different children to name a different day. Do any have a favourite day of the week?
- Show children a circle divided into four. Write *Spring, Summer, Autumn, Winter* round the circle. Remind children that these are the seasons. Discuss which children like best. *Which season are we in now? Autumn.* Talk about the weather in each season.
- Go round each season and write the months – *Spring is March, April, May; Summer June, July, August*, etc.
- Discuss in which season children have birthdays. *What other things happen in this season?*

Activities:

Independent task: Give each child PCM R3. Children work in pairs to complete.

Teacher-monitored task: Work with a group of eight children. Have cards with months of the year, seasons and days of week, plus three plates, labelled 'days of the week', 'months of the year' and 'seasons'. Each child takes a card in turn and decides which plate to put it on – the rest can help if required. Continue until all cards are on plates.

Assessment criteria:

- Can identify days of the week, spoken or written
- Can identify months of the year, spoken or written
- Can identify the seasons, spoken or written

Plenary:

Write *Monday* on the board. Can any children think of something they do specifically on a Monday? Repeat for Saturday then Sunday.

Y2 Review of pre-requisite skills for Block D1.a and D1.b

Objectives:

- Recognise 2D shapes as different from 3D shapes
- Identify some 2D shapes with reference to their properties

Mental oral starter:

Shape search

Children work with a partner. Divide the pairs into two groups – circles and squares. Pairs look round the room for examples of their shape. Partners talk about the examples they see. Give children two or three minutes. Take feedback giving the team points for well-spotted circles or squares.

Teaching sequence:

- Show children an assortment of 2D and 3D shapes. Divide the class into two teams. One team is collecting 3D shapes. *These are all solid. They are not flat like a piece of paper. They roll and stand up, and take up space in the tray*. The other team is collecting 2D shapes. *These are all flat like a piece of paper. They do not take up much space because they are flat.*
- Hold up a shape. *Which team is going to claim it? Is it solid or flat?* Hand the shape to the appropriate team. Continue holding up shapes until all shapes have been claimed by the appropriate team.
- Show three large, easily visible, 2D shapes (square, circle, oblong) on the board. *Are these all the same? No. How are they different?* Encourage children to suggest aspects that make each shape different, for example, that one has corners, that one is round, that one has four sides. Spend time discussing the shapes.
- Point at one shape, for example, a square. *Can you name this shape?* Point at each shape in turn and name – square, circle and oblong.
- *Are there any other shapes you can name?* Encourage children to describe or draw these.

Activities:

Paired activity for the whole class: All children do a simple printing task to create patterns with three 2D shapes: circle, oblong and square. It may be necessary to stagger the start of the task to get different groups going, but once engaged, children can proceed independently. Give each group thick card shapes – circles, squares and oblongs. Children stick a shape to paper with Blu-tac then crayon over with wax crayons, in short strokes out from the centre and onto the paper, all round the shape. They lift the card shape leaving the white shape in the crayoned edge. Children do several in different orientations. Results can be mounted in a display.

Assessment criteria:

- Understand there are 2D and 3D shapes, which are different
- Distinguish and identify square, oblong and circle

Plenary:

Show children a square standing on its corner. *What shape is this?* Take suggestions (some will say 'diamond'). Turn so all children can see it is a square. Stress that a square is a square, whichever way up it is presented.

Y2 Review of pre-requisite skills for Block D1.c and D1.d

Objectives:

- Count backwards from 50
- Say number before any number up to 50
- Count back by the number of units in a number to reach multiple of ten

Mental oral starter:

Blast off!

Count back from 50 with the whole class, ending on *Blast off!* Choose a group of 4/5 children to stand up. Ask a child in the class for a starting number between 5 and 15. The group must count back from that number while the rest of the class listens and checks. At *Blast-off!* the group may jump into the air to indicate a rocket taking off. Repeat with another group, allowing the class to suggest a different starting number. Repeat several times with different groups.

Teaching sequence:

- Show children a 0–49 number grid, in five rows of 10.
- Point at a number and ask children to name it. Repeat several times.
- Choose a child to say a number on the grid. Write on the board. *What is the number before the number on the board?* Encourage children who find this hard to count back in their heads and use the grid.
- Repeat several times, asking different children to pick a number, identifying the number before.
- Ask a child to choose a number on the grid, for example, *35*. Say it together. Write a subtraction on board: *35 – 5* = □. Discuss what the answer will be if we remove 5 from 35. Encourage suggestions.
- Ask children to hold up five fingers. Start at 35 and count back 5, turning down one finger for each number. *We get to 30.* Point at the number grid. Show that 5 less than 35 is 30.
- Repeat, subtracting 7 from 27 by counting back, then 3 from 43.
- Show children a number, for example, 38. *How many will we need to subtract or count back to reach the multiple of ten?* Point at the grid. *How many must we take away from 38 to get back to 30?* Encourage children to see it is '8' – the number of units in the number.

Activities:

Independent task: Give each child PCM R4 to complete individually.

Teacher-monitored task: Give a group of eight children in pairs, a 0–49 grid. Show a number, for example, 36. Children discuss with their partners what we must subtract from this number to be left with a number that ends in 0. Pairs record the subtraction on the whiteboard. Check each has done this correctly. Repeat ten times.

Assessment criteria:

- Can say the number before any number up to 50 while looking at number grid
- Recognise if we count back by number of units in a number, we reach the multiple of ten

Plenary:

Write *105* on the board. Children work with a talking partner to discuss how many we must count back or subtract to reach a number ending in 0. Take suggestions then demonstrate that, if we count back 5, we reach 100.

Y2 Review of pre-requisite skills for Block E1.a and E1.b

Objectives:

- Recognise doubles of numbers up to 5
- Recognise halves of even numbers up to 10

Mental oral starter:

Dicey doubles

Children work in pairs with a whiteboard each. Each child writes three numbers between 2 and 12 on their whiteboard and draws circles round each number (they may write one number twice if they wish). Throw a dice and look how it lands, for example, 3. Place a second dice to show the same number, for example, 3. Ask children the total, for example 3 + 3 = 6. If any pair has that number on their board, they cross it off. The first pair to cross out all their three numbers wins!

Teaching sequence:

- Give out number petals or 'Show me' cards with numbers 1–10, one per child or two children sharing.
- Show children the double 3 domino. *This domino has the same number on each side. Cover one side. How many dots are there on one side? Three.*
- Write *double 3* = □ on the board. Consult the class. *What is double three?* Ask them to show the answer using their number petals. Show the whole domino. *Double three is six.* Point out that there are six dots on the whole domino. Complete the sentence on the board: *double 3 = 6.*
- Show children the double 4 domino, covering one side. *How many dots on this side?* Children show you using their cards. *Four. This is also a double domino – it has the same number of dots on both sides.*
- Write *double 4* = □. *What is double four?* Children show you using their cards. Show the whole domino so that they can check. Complete the sentence on the board: *double 4 = 8.*
- Repeat, showing one side of the double 2 domino, then the whole domino: *double 2 = 4.*
- Repeat, showing one side of the double 5 domino, then the whole domino: *double 5 = 10.*
- Finally, repeat for the double 1 domino.
- Go back through the sentences on the board, reading them aloud together.

Activities:

Paired activity for the whole class: Children work in groups of four. Some support may be required for a few groups, but most groups can complete this independently. Give each group a pile of dominoes – only those with even totals of dots. Children take a domino each and write the total number of dots, then check each other's counting. Each child in the group takes a turn to draw an arrow and write half their number of dots, for example, if their domino has eight dots, they write *8 → 4*. The rest of the group checks their work. Each child repeats the activity with new domino.

Assessment criteria:

- Can double numbers up to 5
- Can halve even numbers up to 10

Plenary:

Show children two dominoes with 16 dots in all. *How might we work out what half this number is?* Give children a few minutes, then show them that we can halve 10 (5) and halve 6 (3).

Y2 Review of pre-requisite skills for Block E1.c and E1.d

Objectives:

- Recognise and identify all British coins
- Calculate amounts of money using two different coins

Mental oral starter:

Counting coins

Show children a pottery mug and a set of 5p and 10p coins. Say that you are going to drop some coins into the mug. Children will shut their eyes and count the 'clinks' as the coins drop into the mug. Drop three coins in. *Open your eyes.* Pairs work together to say how much is in the mug. Remind them that they do not know if the three coins were 10p coins, 5p coins or a mixture. The pairs discuss this then make some suggestions. Show them that it could be 15p (three 5p coins), 30p (three 10p coins), 20p (two 5p coins, one 10p) or 25p (two 10p coins, one 5p).

Teaching sequence:

- Show children one of each type of coin from 1p to £2. Use large coins so that they can all see. Pass round real coins so that children can see the real sizes.
- Discuss the differences. *Which coins are silver? 5p, 10p, 20p, 50p. Which coins are gold? £1 and £2. Which coins are copper (brown)? 1p and 2p.* Point out that gold coins are worth the most, then the silver coins, then the copper or brown coins.
- Give each child a coin to hold – not the £1 and £2 coins. Name the coin, for example, *ten pence*. Children holding a 10p coin hold it up in the air. Repeat, naming different coins.
- Choose two children holding different coins, for example, 20p and 2p. Discuss how much they have in total. Write the addition: *20p + 2p =* □. Discuss how we do this. Complete the addition: *20p + 2p = 22p*.
- Repeat, choosing two children holding different coins, for example, 5p and 50p. Discuss how much they have in total. Write the addition: *50p + 5p =* □. *We have fifty and five pence, making fifty-five pence in all.* Complete the addition: *50p + 5p = 55p.*
- Repeat several times, choosing different pairs and adding their coins.

Activities:

Independent task: Give children a copy of PCM R5 to complete individually.

Teacher-monitored task: Work with a group of six children. Have 1p, 2p, 5p, 10p, 20p, 50p coins ready in a cloth bag. Each child takes two coins without showing the others. Each child in turn looks at their coins and says the total. The others have to guess what the two coins are. Go round the table, then replace the coins in the bag. Repeat six times.

Assessment criteria:

- Recognise and be able to name all coins
- Can add two coins less than £1 and say total

Plenary:

Draw some coins on the flip chart. Using two of these coins, *what is the lowest amount we could have? What is the highest?*

Y2 Review of pre-requisite skills for Block A2.a and A2.b

Objectives:

- Recognise numbers 1–100
- Say a number 1 more or less than any number <100
- Say a number 10 more or less than any number <100

Mental oral starter:

Reverse numbers

Ask children to draw a 3 × 3 grid on a page. You draw the same on the board. Write a 2-digit number. Children must write the number with the digits reversed in the matching space on their grid, for example, you write 36, they write 63. Continue writing numbers on each row of the grid. Point at the first number you wrote. Ask one child to say their number aloud. Do others think they are correct? Continue, checking that children can say numbers correctly.

Teaching sequence:

- Show children a 1–100 grid. Choose a number, for example, 58, and say it. Ask a child to identify this number on the grid. Ask other children: *Have they pointed at the right number?*
- Ask children what the next number is. *What is one more than fifty-eight?* Demonstrate on the grid that one more than 58 is 59. *We move along the row to find the number one more. This is the next number, or the number after.*
- Ask children what the number before 58 is. *What is one less than fifty-eight?* Demonstrate on the grid that one less than 58 is 57. *We move backwards along the row to find the number one less. This is the number before.*
- Ask: *What is ten more than fifty-eight?* Demonstrate on the grid that ten more than 58 is 68. *We move down the grid to find the number ten more. This is ten more than fifty-eight, or fifty-eight add ten.*
- Ask: *What is ten less than fifty-eight?* Demonstrate on the grid that ten less than 58 is 48. *We move up the grid to find the number ten less. This is ten less than fifty-eight or fifty-eight take away ten.*
- Repeat with a new number, finding ten more, ten less, one more, one less.

Activities:

Independent task: Give children a copy of PCM R6. They complete this working individually.

Teacher-monitored task: Meanwhile, sit with a group of 8–10 children round a table, with TU place-value cards and a large 1–100 grid. Give each child one tens card and one units card. They create a 2-digit number. Ask each child to say the number one more than their number, using the grid to help. Repeat, asking for the number one less than their number, then ten more than their number, then ten less than their number. Replace the cards and give each child another two. Repeat six times.

Assessment criteria:

- Can say a number one more or one less than any 2-digit number, using 1–100 grid
- Can say a number ten more or ten less than any 2-digit number, using 1–100 grid

Plenary:

Write *43* on the board. Challenge children to tell their partner the number eleven less. *What about eleven more?*

Y2 Review of pre-requisite skills for Block A2.c and A2.d

Objectives:

- Order any three numbers up to 50
- Say a number in-between two others up to 50

Mental oral starter:

Which way round?

Put children in pairs. Ask each child to write a number between 1 and 30. Pairs work to write their two numbers in order, smaller then larger, on their board and hold it up. Challenge each pair to write a number between the two numbers then show you.

Teaching sequence:

- Show children a large pegged number line, 1–30. Together, count along the line, pointing at each number as they say it.
- Ask children to turn their backs to the line. Remove three numbers. Children then turn back. Ask each to write the three missing numbers on their board.
- *Which is the smallest?* Count along the line till you reach the first space. *Which number is this?* Point out that this is the smallest because it is nearest the beginning of the line.
- Repeat to identify the largest number, nearest the end of the line, and the middle number. Replace the numbers on the line.
- Show children a 1–50 number grid, in five rows of ten. Children shut their eyes or turn round. Cover six numbers using Post-It Notes.
- Children open their eyes. *Which of the missing numbers is the smallest? How do you know?* Point out that we do not even need to know what the number is. It must be smallest because it is nearest the top of the grid and the start of the row.
- *Which of the missing numbers is the largest? How do you know?* Point out again that we do not need to know what the number is. It must be the largest because it is nearest the bottom of the grid and the end of the row.
- Discuss which the other missing numbers are. How do children know? Reveal each number as it is identified.

Activities:

Independent task: Children work in pairs. Provide each child with a copy of PCM R7. Children complete, discussing with partner.

Teacher-monitored task: Sit with a group of eight children at a table, with 1–50 number cards. Give each child two cards. Children lay their cards on the table face up. Ask each child to write a number between their two on their whiteboard. Together, check everyone's number. Children replace the cards and take two more. Repeat ten times.

Assessment criteria:

- Can put numbers up to 50 in order on a line
- Can fill in missing numbers on a 1–50 grid
- Can order any three numbers up to 50
- Can write number between two numbers up to 50

Plenary:

Write a number in letters on board, for example *sixty-five*. Can children show this number written in figures on their whiteboard? Repeat.

Y2 Review of pre-requisite skills for Block B2.a and B2.b

Objectives:

- Add two numbers both less than 8 without counting on
- Know that, if we add 0, it leaves a number unchanged

Mental oral starter:

Add four

Children work in pairs. Each pair writes three numbers from 5 to 10 on their whiteboard and draws a circle round each. Throw a large dice. *We will add four to the dice throw.* Encourage the children to show the total on their fingers, for example, if the dice number is 3, adding 4 makes 7, so they show 7 fingers. If any pair of children has that number written on their whiteboard, they may cross it out! Keep playing like this until one pair has crossed off all their numbers. Bingo! They win.

Teaching sequence:

- Use playing cards 1–7. Give each child a card, but explain that two 'special' children have no card.
- Ask two children to stand up. Each says their number, for example, *five* and *four.* Write these numbers as an addition on the board, *5 + 4 =* □.
- Ask the class to work out what the sum is, using their fingers if necessary. Discuss how many different ways there are to work out the answer. We could
  (i) add four and four, then add one extra
  (ii) add five and five, then take one off
  (iii) add two to five, then add two more
  (iv) count on in ones.
- Point out that the last way is the slowest. Record the addition on the board: *5 + 4 = 9.*
- Choose two different children, for example, holding 3 and 7. Record the addition on the board: *3 + 7 =* □. Discuss how to do the addition. *We could add three and three and then add four more, but this is probably not the easiest way.* Discuss different ways to choose to do this addition.
- Choose two new children and do the addition of cards, discussing different ways to do it.
- Choose one child with a card, and one without. Write the number, for example, 6, on the board. Point at the child with no card. *We are adding nothing! Write 6 + 0 =* □. Consult the class. Remind children that adding nothing or zero leaves the number unchanged. Point at a second child with no card. *What happens if we add zero twice? Nothing. Write 6 + 0 + 0 = 6. We can add zero as many times as we like. It leaves the number unchanged.*

Activities:

Independent task: Give each child a copy of PCM 11 to complete.

Teacher-monitored task: Give eight children red and yellow cubes. Ask each child to use both colours to make a tower of nine cubes. Record the different numbers of coloured cubes, for example, 2 red and 7 yellow. Each child writes their own addition. Go round recording the different ways we can make nine. Repeat to make eight cubes with two different colours.

Assessment criteria:

- Add two numbers less than 8 without counting on
- Add 0 to a number; know this leaves the number unchanged

Plenary:

Ask children to find different additions where the answer is 6. Encourage some to add more than two numbers.

Y2 Review of pre-requisite skills for Block B2.c and B2.d

Objectives:

- Recognise concept of turning
- Know left and right
- Move in different directions

Mental oral starter:

Left, right …

Draw a 3 × 3 grid on the board. Write *2, 7, 6* along the top row, *9, 5, 1* along the second row, and *4, 3, 8* along the bottom row. Point at the 3, and say the number. Ask children to show you on their fingers the number to the right of 3. This should be eight fingers. Discuss the fact that the right is further along the row. Point at the 3 again. Ask children to show you their fingers to match the number to the left – four fingers. Repeat with 5, asking for the number to the right, then the number to the left. Repeat for 7.

Teaching sequence:

- Draw a 5 × 5 grid on the board. Blu-tac a card or felt mouse to the bottom left square; a piece of cheese to the top right square; and a card cat to the top left square.
- Explain that the hungry mouse has to reach the cheese! *We shall need to give it instructions. Be careful or the mouse may wind up in the cat's paws.*
- Model the type of instructions. Say clearly: *Mouse – move one space forward.* Make the mouse move one grid square forward. *Mouse, turn to the left.* Make the mouse turn to the left.
- Say: *Mouse move one square forward.* Point out which way the mouse is facing. *If it goes forward now, which way will it move? To the left.* Demonstrate to children.
- Continue, encouraging children to join in. *We need to give an instruction to the mouse to make her turn. Which way do we want her to turn?* Discuss with the class.
- Remind children of left and right. *It is very helpful to know which is left and which is right otherwise our mouse may wind up in the cat's paws! We can help ourselves remember by looking at our hands.* Hold your hands out, with the backs of your hands facing you. Ask children to do the same. Spread out your thumbs. Ask children to do the same. *Look at your left hand. The thumb and hand form the letter L for left!*
- Children use this to help give the mouse instructions to get to the cheese, not to the cat!

Activities:

Paired activity for the whole class: In pairs, write numbers to fill two 4 × 4 grids – both pairs creating the same grid, so the numbers must be the same. Children turn so that they cannot see other's grid, then give each other instructions. For example, the first child says: *Colour in red the number to the left of 6*, and both do this. The second child says: *Colour in blue the number to the right of 14*, and both do this. Children continue until all the numbers are coloured. Have they both followed the instructions correctly? Are their grids coloured the same?

Assessment criteria:

- Know which way is left and which way is right
- Understand concept of a turn
- Understand movement in different directions

Plenary:

Show a clock-face. Point out that the hands <u>turn</u> on the face. Demonstrate forwards (clockwise) and backwards (anti-clockwise) turns. Children show a 'thumbs up' for a forwards turn and a 'thumbs down' for a backwards turn.

Y2 Review of pre-requisite skills for Block C2.a and C2.b

Objectives:

- Measure weight of objects using non-standard uniform weights
- Compare weights of different things using non-standard measurements

Mental oral starter:

Animals like me

Give each child a whiteboard. They draw an animal they think would weigh the same as they do! They need to think and discuss with a talking partner. Praise sensible discussion. Give a few minutes then take feedback. Which animals are in the right ballpark? (small sheep, medium dog, badger)

Teaching sequence:

- Show children a large potato and a large cooking apple close in weight. *Which of these is heavier?* Pass round and let children feel weights.
- Take guesses as to which is heavier. *Hands up those who think the potato is heavier.* Write the total on the board. *Hands up those who think the apple is heavier.* Write the total on the board.
- Discuss how to find out. *We will measure the weight of each one using cubes.*
- Show children a set of balances. Place the potato on one side. Count number of multilink cubes it takes to balance the potato. Record on the board. *The potato weighs 30 cubes.*
- Repeat to find the weight of the apple in cubes. *The apple weighs 27 cubes.*
- Compare the two. *Which is heavier? The potato.* Confirm by placing the potato and the apple on the scales.
- Show children a large orange. *Is this heavier than the potato? Than the apple? Because we know what each of these weigh in cubes, we can find out.*
- Place the orange on one side of the balances. Count the number of cubes it takes to balance. Record on the board. *The orange weighs 22 cubes.*
- Point out we now know that the orange is lighter than potato and apple. Stress that weighing things using smaller things such as cubes can be useful to compare more than two things.

Activities:

Grouped activity for the whole class: Children work in threes. Each group has a potato, an apple and an orange. They use cubes and balances to weigh each using multilink cubes. They record weights of each carefully, for example, *potato: 24 cubes*. Have a class discussion about which is the heaviest item in class. *Which is the lightest? Which are in the middle – neither heavy nor light?*

Assessment criteria:

- Can weigh things using non-standard uniform weights
- Can compare weight of things using non-standard measurements

Plenary:

Show a large book to the class. Ask children how many cubes the book might weigh. Children talk to a partner and estimate. Weigh the book in multilink cubes. *How many is it? Whose guess was closest?*

Y2 Review of pre-requisite skills for Block C2.c and C2.d

Objectives:

- Organise information in simple tables
- Use tally marks to quantify information

Mental oral starter:

Favourite day

Give each child a whiteboard. Ask them to write their favourite day. On the board, write the days as column headings in a table. Go round and count the number of votes for each day. Write the number under each heading. *Which day got most votes? Which day got least votes?* Draw children's attention to how we have recorded the information.

Teaching sequence:

- Explain to children we shall make a chart to show the letters their names start with.
- Draw a table of two rows, two columns to start with (leave room: you will add columns). Explain that we are talking about our first names – not surnames. Write 'letter' in the left hand space in the first row. Write 'number of names' in the left hand space in the second row.

Letter	a	b	d	g
Number of names	|||					||

- Ask if anyone's name begins with 'a'? Count the number of children who do. Write 'a' in the first row and record the number of names below using tally marks.
- Continue through the alphabet, using tally marks and recording the number of names beginning with each letter. Do not record letters with no names. Demonstrate how tally marks work – showing how we record five as a bar.
- Look at chart. *Which letters have most names? Which letters have no names? Only one name? What are common letters for names to begin with?*

Activities:

Independent task: Using PCM R8, pairs throw a dice and record each throw with a tally mark. Remind them how to record five using tallies.

Teacher-monitored task: In a group of eight, each child has a chart with two rows and eleven columns. Use a pack of playing cards. *We write the card number in the first space in the top row, and number of cards in the first space in the second row.* Children number the column headings 1 to 10. Children each take a card and record the number with a tally mark below that number on the chart. Go round and give each child a new card. Always replace the cards once recorded. Repeat twenty times. Children compare their charts.

Assessment criteria:

- Understand how to organise information using a table and tally marks

Plenary:

Look at two or three children's tally charts from the card sorting game. *Which cards seem to be coming up the most?* Discuss how many cards there are to choose from. *Are some cards more likely to be taken? (No!).*

Y2 Review of pre-requisite skills for Block D2.a and D2.b

Objectives:

- Recognise 3D shapes as different from 2D shapes
- Identify and correctly name cubes, cylinders and spheres
- Recognise spheres and cylinders are different from circles, cubes are different from squares

Mental oral starter:

Solid drawing

Children work on the whiteboard. Show a cylinder. Ask them to draw it. Tell children you know this is hard – just do their best! Give three or four minutes, then have a go yourself. Look at the drawings. Who has managed to convey the fact that they are drawing a solid shape well? Discuss the fact that it is hard because we are not drawing a flat shape like a square or a circle. We are drawing a solid shape.

Teaching sequence:

- Show children an assortment of thin flat shapes. Point out that these are all flat. *We call these 2D shapes because they are flat.* Identify some of these shapes by name, for example, square, rectangle, circle, triangle.
- Show children an assortment of 3D shapes. Point out that these are all solid. *They are not flat like 2D shapes. They roll and stand up, and take up space.*
- Show children a ball or a sphere. *What do we call this shape? We call it a sphere.* Explain that sphere is the mathematical name for a round ball.
- Ask children to describe the properties of a sphere. Explain that properties of a shape are what make us able to identify it. *A sphere is round and smooth. It rolls. It has no flat faces. It has no corners.* List the properties on the board. *No other shape has all these properties.*
- Show a cylinder. *What do we call this shape? We call it a cylinder.* Explain that cylinder is the mathematical name for the shape of a tin of beans!
- Ask children to describe the properties of a cylinder. Remind them that the properties of a shape are what make us able to identify it. *A cylinder is round, but it also has two flat faces. It can roll but it can also slide on its flat faces. Like the sphere, it has no corners.* List the properties on the board. *No other shape has all these properties.*
- Show children a cube. Remind them what we call this shape. *A cube. What are the properties of a cube? It has six flat faces. It has eight corners. Each face is a square. It does not roll. It can slide.* List the properties on the board.
- Show children a circle and a square. *These are flat shapes. They are 2D shapes.* Demonstrate the difference between a solid sphere and a flat circle, and the difference between a solid cube and a flat square. Pass round all four shapes so the children can see what we mean by solid. *The solid cube has square faces, but it is solid.*

Activities:

Paired activity for the whole class: Children do a simple sorting task to check their knowledge of the difference between flat and solid shapes. Children sort a variety of plastic 2D and 3D shapes into two sets – solid and flat shapes. In pairs, they identify spheres, cylinders and cubes. It may be helpful to rotate children. Those waiting can complete PCM R9.

Assessment criteria:

- Understand that 2D shapes are different from 3D shapes.
- Identify cube, cylinder and sphere
- Understand how we identify shapes by looking at their properties

Plenary:

Ask children to look round the classroom for any spheres, cylinders or cubes. Give praise for each sighting.

Y2 Review of pre-requisite skills for Block D2.c and D2.d

Objectives:

- Count back in tens from any 2-digit number
- Say a number ten less than any 2-digit number

Mental oral starter:

Ten less

Draw a 3 × 3 grid on the board. Children draw a 3 × 3 grid in their books. Explain that you will write a number in the top left square; children will write a number ten less than this in the top left square on their grid. Then you will write another number in the middle of the top row; they will write a number ten less in the middle of the top row on their grid. You will continue until you all have a full grid. Go along the grid, and check the numbers children should have written.

Teaching sequence:

- Show children a 1–100 grid. Ask them to shut their eyes. Cover a number with Post-It Note. Can children say the number?
- Draw a cross on the board.

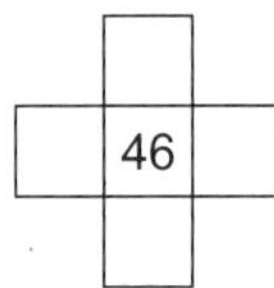

- Explain this is a cross from the number grid. *What number will we write below 46? We will write 56, because as we go down the grid we are counting on in 10s. What number will we write above 46? We will write 36, because as we go up the grid we are counting back in 10s.* Help children to fill out numbers to the left and right of 46, pointing out that as we go along the grid we are counting on in ones.
- Find a number on grid, for example, 72. Ask children to count back in 10s from this number. Children recite, *62, 52, 42*, etc. Point at the numbers on the grid.
- Choose two children. Write *84* on the board. Ask them to count back in 10s from 84. As they say the numbers, write on the board: *84, 74, 64, 54, 44, 34, 24, 14, 4*. Point out that the units digit remains the same when we are counting back in 10s.
- Repeat, choosing two different children to count back in 10s from 97. Point out that the units digit is always 7.

Activities:

Independent task: Give each child a copy of PCM R10 to complete with a talking partner.

Teacher-monitored task: Arrange a group of eight children in pairs and give each pair a 1–100 number line. Remove a number, for example, 73 from the line. Children discuss with partners which number is ten less than this number. Each child writes numbers counting back in 10s from the original number, for example, *73, 63, 53*, etc. Children check their partner's sequences. Remind them that the units digit should not change. Repeat six times.

Assessment criteria:

- Say number ten less than any 2-digit number
- Can count back in tens from any 2-digit number

Plenary:

Write *115* on the board. Children work in pairs to find out which number is ten less than this number. Take suggestions and model finding out that 115 – 10 = 105. Repeat to find ten less than 105. Discuss the answer.

Y2 Review of pre-requisite skills for Block E2.a and E2.b

Objectives:

- Count in 2s from 0 to 20 and back
- Count in 5s from 0 to 50 and back

Mental oral starter:

Counting in fives

Show children a mug with a 5p coin in it. Agree that there is 5p in the mug. Show them some 5p coins. Explain that they will count how much is in the mug as you add some 5p coins. Ask all children to turn round and shut their eyes. They must listen very carefully! Clearly drop one, then another, then another, then another coin in the mug.
Ask children to open their eyes. How much do they think is in the mug? Ask each pair of children to write the amount on a whiteboard. *Who is correct?* Repeat this several times, dropping different numbers of 5p coins into the mug which starts with 5p in it. Try starting with 10p in the mug and repeating this.

Teaching sequence:

- Show children a 1–20 number line. *We will count along this in twos. We will remove the numbers that we say!*
- Children count slowly in twos: *two, four, six, etc.* At the same time, remove these numbers and give them to different children. At 20, stop and keep number 20 for yourself.
- Show children 20. *If I start here and count back in twos, what number will I say next?* Encourage children to realise that it is eighteen. *Who is holding 18?* The child stands. *If we are counting back in twos, what number will we say next? Sixteen*. The child holding 16 stands.
- Continue counting back in twos, with children standing as their number is spoken.
- Count up in twos, asking the children to sit down as their number is spoken.
- Hand out numbers 5, 15, 20 … 45 to those who are not holding multiples of two. ***Note:*** some children will already be holding multiples of 5, which are also multiples of 2, e.g. 10.
- *We shall count in fives from five*. Ask the child holding 5 to stand up. *What number will we say next if we are counting in fives?* Encourage all children to count slowly in fives. As they do, children holding each number stand up. Encourage discussion on why some children stand up both for multiples of 10 and 2.
- Repeat to count back in fives from fifty to five.

Activities:

Individual task: Give each child PCM R13. The children play this in pairs.

Teacher-monitored task: Work with eight children. Use cards 5–50 (2 sets) and cards 2–20 (2 sets). Shuffle these and give two cards to each child. Spread the remaining cards face up on table. *We are going to produce a line of twos and a line of fives*. Ask the child holding 2 to lay the first card in the twos line. Ask child holding 5 to lay the first card in the fives line. Ask children holding the next number in each line (4 and 10) to lay their cards. Continue to create a line of twos and a line of fives. If no one has the next number, look in the cards face up on the table. *Is it there?* The first child to get rid of all their cards takes a cube. Play again – who gets a cube this time?

Assessment criteria:

- Can count in twos from 0 to 20 and back
- Can count in fives from 0 to 50 and back

Plenary:

Write *102* and *105* on the board. *If we counted in twos or fives long enough, would we reach either of these numbers?* Challenge children to explain their answer.

Y2 Review of pre-requisite skills for Block E2.c and E2.d

Objectives:

- Understand we can count in 'lots of' any number

Mental oral starter:

Counting in twos

Write *6* on the board. Ask children how many twos you have to count to reach this number. Demonstrate this using your fingers: *two, four, six* (three fingers). *I counted three twos.* Tell them to show you three fingers. *This is correct.* Write *10* on the board. This time do not help them. *How many twos did I have to count to reach ten?* Encourage the children to count in twos using their fingers. They should be showing five fingers. Encourage them to show you five on their fingers and not shout out. Repeat by writing *16* on board, then *12*, then *20.*

Teaching sequence:

- Show children a 1–40 number line (preferably on an interactive whiteboard).
- Discuss the fact that we can count along the number line in ones. Show them, counting swiftly in unison.
- Remind children that we can also count along the line in twos. Choose six children to stand up and count along the line in twos, starting at 2. Point at the numbers on the line as they say them.
- *Now we are going to count along the line in threes. This is a little harder.* Draw hops along the line to help children realise which number to say next. *3, 6, 9 …*
- Point at the hops drawn along the line. *This shows us hopping in threes. We can draw in hops of any number, for example, we could hop in fours or fives or sixes.*
- Show a new number line and draw hops along it to enable you to count in fours. Children say the numbers as you draw the hops: *four, eight, twelve, sixteen …*
- Discuss how drawing different hops along a number line could help. Show children three purses. *Each purse has 4p in it. I want to know how much I have.* Point at the line where you hopped in fours. *I can count three fours. Four, eight, twelve. Three hops of four is twelve. I have 12p.*
- Repeat the process to show that, if we have six purses with 3p in each, we can count six hops of 3 along the number line to reach 18. *We have 18p.*

Activities:

Independent task: Give each child a copy of PCM 107. They colour in every fourth square, counting in fours, starting at 4: 4, 8, 12, etc. Encourage them to work with a partner and be very careful.

Teacher-monitored task: Give each child in a group of six a 1–20 number line. You use three mugs and 2p coins. Place 4p in each mug and ask each child to count in fours along their line to tell you how much you have in all. They count *4, 8, 12.* Make sure all children follow how to do this. Repeat to ask children how much there is if you have five mugs with 3p in each, etc. Choose amounts that require children to count in different hops.

Assessment criteria:

- Can count along number line to 40 in hops of different sizes

Plenary:

Write *15* on the board. Ask children, in pairs, to discuss how many hops of three are needed to reach this number. *How many hops of five are needed?*

Y2 Review of pre-requisite skills for Block A3.a and A3.b

Objectives:

- Read and write numbers up to 100 in figures
- Identify tens and units in 2-digit number

Mental oral starter:

Guess my number

Put children in pairs. Say that you have a number between 1 and 50 in your pocket. Children work in pairs to guess the number: they ask questions, you give clues, for example, *It is less than 25. It has two digits*. Play several times and then let a confident child 'hide' a number.

Teaching sequence:

- Write *48* on the board. Ask children to read the number. Show them large 10p coins and 1p coins. Write *48p* on board. *How will we make this amount using these coins?*
- *Which figure shows how many 10p coins to take?* Discuss. *Which figure shows how many 1p coins to take?* Point out that forty-eight, means we need forty pence, which is four tens. Take four 10p coins, pointing at '4'. *This shows us how many tens.*
- Point at '8' in 48. *This shows us how many 1p coins to take. Forty-eight is four tens and eight ones.* Take eight 1p coins. Show children that we have forty (4 × 10) and eight (8 × 1).
- Turn the digits round and write 84 on the board. Ask children to read it. *This is eighty-four.* Point out that it has the same digits as 48, but is not same number.
- *How many 10p coins must we take to have 84p?* Point at '8'. *This is eighty. We need eight 10p coins to give us eighty pence.* Take eight 10p coins, counting in tens to show that you have eighty pence.
- Point at '4' in 84p. *How many 1p coins must we take to have 84p? We need four 1p coins to give us eighty-four pence.* Take four 1p coins, counting in ones to show that you have four pence.
- Demonstrate using coins that you now have 84p.
- Stress that 84p and 48p have the same digits, but are not the same number. *One has eight 10p coins and four 1p coins; the other has four 10p coins and eight 1p coins. Which is more?*
- Repeat to show the difference between 36p and 63p.

Activities:

Independent task: Give children a copy of PCM 4 to complete individually.

Teacher-monitored task: Meanwhile, sit with a group of eight children at a table, with 0–9 number cards. Each child takes two, placing them together to create a 2-digit number. Children take turns to read the numbers aloud. Have piles of 10p and 1p coins. Each child matches their number to the appropriate coins, for example, if they have 24, they take two 10p and four 1p coins. Go round and check. Ask each child to reverse the digits. *What number do you have now? How will you need to adjust your coins?* Repeat six times.

Assessment criteria:

- Can identify any 2-digit number
- Can understand tens and units digits in 2-digit number

Plenary:

Write *98* on the board. Encourage children to reverse the digits and write the new number. *How many more is 98 than the new number?* Children count in ones to find out.

Y2 Review of pre-requisite skills for Block A3.c and A3.d

Objectives:

- Count on from a 2-digit number to a second 2-digit number
- Add a 1-digit number to a 2-digit number by counting on

Mental oral starter:

Count on …

Put children in pairs. Each pair writes four numbers from 0 to 9 on their whiteboard. Write *24* on the board. Throw a dice. *We will add the dice throw to the number.* Pairs do this by counting on from 24. If a number on their board equals the units digit in the answer, they cross it out. Continue with different starting numbers, throwing the dice, adding by counting on and seeing what the units digit is. Which pair is first to cross out all their numbers? Bingo!

Teaching sequence:

- Show children a large 1–50 number grid, in rows of ten. Choose a child to identify a number on the grid, for example, *26*. The class all read the number.
- Choose another child to take a card from a pile of cards 2–9, for example, *5. We shall add this number to 26.* Write the addition: *26 + 5 =* □. Discuss how we know what the total is. *We shall count on.*
- Point at the 5. Ask children to show five fingers. *This is how much we are adding*. Point at a number on the grid, for example, *26. We start here.* Say *twenty-six* then count on, folding down one finger for each number. *Thirty-one*. Complete the addition: *26 + 5 = 31*. Read together.
- Repeat this activity.
- Choose a child to select a number on the grid. Say it together, for example, *78*. Select a number about 5 or 6 larger and point to it. Say the number with children, for example, *84*. Write both on the board.
- Consult the class. *How many must we count to get from the smaller number to the larger? How much bigger is the larger number than the smaller?* Show how we find out by counting from 78 to 84, holding up one finger for each number, *79, 80, 81, 82, 83, 84. That's six fingers. 84 is six larger than 78. If we add six to 78, we get 84.*
- Repeat to show how much larger 53 is than 49.

Activities:

Independent task: Give each child a copy of PCM 78 to complete. If they find this easy, provide PCM 79.

Teacher-monitored task: Sit with a group of eight children at a table, in pairs, with a number grid for each pair. Each pair chooses a number on the grid and writes it on their whiteboard, then chooses a number in the row below, for example, they choose 46, then choose any number beginning with '5'. Each pair works together to find the difference between two numbers. Repeat six times.

Assessment criteria:

- Can add a 1-digit number to a 2-digit number by counting on
- Can count on from one 2-digit number to another

Plenary:

Write a number, for example, *24*. Ask children to reverse the digits and say the number, for example, *42*. *How many must we count to get from the smaller to the larger?*

Y2 Review of pre-requisite skills for Block B3.a and B3.b

Objectives:

- Know names of common 2D and 3D shapes
- Identify common shapes by reference to properties

Mental oral starter:

Squares and triangles

Draw a square on the board. Children draw a square on their whiteboards. Can they draw a line across the square to divide it into two triangles? Give them a minute to think, then share the method. *We have to draw a line from corner to corner.* Can they divide their square into two rectangles? Give them a minute to discuss, then take feedback.

Teaching sequence:

- Show children a square, an oblong, a cube and a sphere. Can they identify the flat shapes? Can they identify the solid shapes? Remind children that we call flat shapes 2D shapes, and we call solid shapes 3D shapes. *The flat shapes are the square and the rectangle. The solid shapes are the cube and the sphere.*
- On the board show children a square, a rectangle, a triangle and a circle. Ask them if they can name any of these. Assist children in identifying each shape by name.
- *I have a shape in my pocket. It is one of these four. I am going to give you some clues to help you all say which shape it is. It has four corners.* (Prevent children shouting out guesses.) *It has four sides. Two of the sides are long, and two of the sides are short.* Hopefully, children can now guess correctly.
- Repeat with a different 2D shape.
- Show children a large example of a cube, a sphere, a cylinder and a pyramid. Ask children if they can name any of these. Assist children in identifying each shape by name.
- *I have a shape in my pocket. It is one of these four. I am going to give you some clues to help you all say which shape it is. It has two flat faces. It has one round side. Two of the faces are circles. It will roll but it could also slide.* Hopefully, children can now guess correctly.
- Repeat with a different 3D shape.

Activities:

Independent task: Children complete PCM 60 and PCM 61 in pairs.

Teacher-monitored task: Children work in groups of eight. Have a selection of flat and solid shapes in a cloth bag. Allow each child in turn to withdraw a shape without showing the others, then describe some of its properties so the others can identify it. First, a child says if it is a 2D or 3D shape, then gives details of its other properties until the others guess correctly. Keep going until every child has had a turn.

Assessment criteria:

- Recognise common 2D/3D shape by name
- Understand that we identify shapes by reference to their properties

Plenary:

Show the side of a cube, flat edge on, from over a portable whiteboard. Can children guess what shape this is? It could be a cube or a rectangle or a square! Show children that it is a cube. Repeat with a sphere. *Could this be a circle?*

Y2 Review of pre-requisite skills for Block B3.c and B3.d

Objectives:

- Know pairs of numbers that make 6, 7, 8 and 9

Mental oral starter:

Make 7

Draw a 2 × 2 grid on the board. Children draw the same on their whiteboard. Explain that you will write a number on your grid, then they have to write the number that goes with it to make 7 in the matching space on their grid. For example, you write 4, they write 3. Continue until the grids are full, then check children's answers.

Teaching sequence:

- Show children a large dice. Point out that the opposite faces always add up to the same number. Demonstrate this. Show children the one dot. *Which number is opposite this? Six dots. One and six make seven.* Demonstrate for the other opposite faces.
- Write all the additions on the board: *1 + 6 = 7, 2 + 5 = 7, 3 + 4 = 7*. Rehearse these with children.
- Show children the 4 + 4 domino. *How many dots in total? Eight. Are there any other dominoes that have eight dots in total?* Encourage children to consider this with a partner. Show and record all the other dominoes with eight dots: *6 + 2, 5 + 3*.
- Point at all the additions that total 8. *Are we missing any possible pairs?* Demonstrate that we have *4 + 4, 3 + 5, 2 + 6* but not *1 + something*. Encourage children to realise that we need 1 + 7 = 8. Rehearse all the ways of making 8.
- Repeat with a domino with six dots, for example 3 + 3. *This domino has six dots. Can you think of other dominoes that will have six dots?* Encourage children to suggest 1 + 5, 2 + 4. Record their answers.
- Show children the 6 + 0 domino. *This has six dots as well.* Add 6 + 0 to the list of additions where the total is 6. Look back at the additions where the total is 7 or 8. *Which additions are we missing?* Add 7 + 0 = 7, and 8 + 0 = 8 to the appropriate lists.

Activities:

Independent task: Give children PCM R11 to work on individually.

Teacher-monitored task: Meanwhile, sit a group of eight children at one/two tables, each child with a whiteboard. From a set of 0–9 number cards, give each child a card. Each child writes the number which, when added to their card number, makes 9, for example, if a child has 4, they write 5. Go round the group, each child showing the others their pair of numbers. *Are they correct?* Repeat at least six times.

Assessment criteria:

- Recognise pairs of numbers making 6
- Recognise pairs of numbers making 7
- Recognise pairs of numbers making 8
- Recognise pairs of numbers making 9

Plenary:

Write *2, 6, 4, 8* on the board. Ask children to add two numbers very quickly. They show you their answers on their fingers or using a whiteboard. Challenge them to say which pair they have added.

Y2 Review of pre-requisite skills for Block C3.a and C3.b

Objectives:

- Begin to use and understand vocabulary of capacity
- Understand how we compare capacities using uniform non-standard measure

Mental oral starter:

Which holds more?

Give each child a whiteboard. Show children a glass and mug. *Which one holds the most?* They must discuss then draw the one they think holds the most. Fill the glass with lentils. Show children it is full. Tip the contents into the mug. *Do the lentils fill the mug? Does the glass still have some in it when the mug is full?* Agree with children which holds more, the glass or mug.

Teaching sequence:

- Show children a teapot, a bottle and a jug. *Which holds more, the bottle, the jug or the teapot?* Ask pairs to discuss, and take suggestions.
- Explain the easiest way to find out is to measure each using the same measure. Show children a yoghurt pot. *We can count how many small pots will fill each container. This will tell us which is the largest.*
- Fill the teapot with coloured water. Ask a child to hold the yoghurt pot over a large bowl in case of spillages. Ask the class to sit and stand so they can all see.
- Fill the yoghurt pot as many times as possible from the teapot. Encourage children to count the number of yoghurt pots the teapot fills. Record on the board. *The teapot fills 8 pots.*
- Show children the jug and fill it with coloured water. Use the jug to fill as many yoghurt pots as possible. Ask children to count how many pots the jug will fill. Record on the board. *The jug fills 6 pots.*
- Show children the bottle and fill it with coloured water. Use the bottle to fill as many yoghurt pots as possible. Record the number of pots filled by the bottle. *The bottle fills 9 pots.*
- Point at all three statements. *Which container filled the most yoghurt pots? The bottle. The bottle is the largest. Which container filled fewest yoghurt pots? This one is the smallest.* Stress it is possible to measure the capacity of a container using a smaller pot as a measure.

Activities:

Paired activity for the whole class: all children rotate through a simple measuring task. Use a variety of containers and ask small groups of children to measure their container in yoghurt pots. Each writes an estimate. *I think it will fill □ pots.* They fill their container with lentils/water. *How many yoghurt pots does it fill?* They compare the total with the estimate. *Whose guess was closest?*

Assessment criteria:

- Understand that we can use a small container as a measure of a larger container's capacity
- Compare capacities using non-standard measure

Plenary:

Show a thermos flask. Discuss how many pots will fill it. Take suggestions, then fill using the pots. Was it fewer than children thought?

Y2 Review of pre-requisite skills for Block C3.c and C3.d

Objectives:

- Subtract a 1-digit number from multiple of ten
- Rehearse pairs of numbers that make ten

Mental oral starter:

Add to ten

In pairs, children write four numbers from 0 to 10 on whiteboards and draw a circle round each. Shuffle 0–10 number cards. Show the top one. If a pair has a number on the whiteboard that adds to the card number to make ten, they cross it out. Continue. The first pair to cross out all their numbers wins. Bingo!

Teaching sequence:

- Remind children of pairs of numbers that make ten. Write on the board: *1 + 9, 2 + 8, 3 + 7, 4 + 6, 5 + 5*. Rehearse by chanting aloud.
- Show children a 1–100 grid. Count down the multiples of ten. Agree how many tens are in each one, for example, *Seventy is seven tens, thirty is three tens.*
- Point at one multiple of ten, for example, 60. Use to create a subtraction: *60 – 4 =* □. Read together. Discuss how we can work this out. *Can we use the grid to help us? We can count back from the multiple of ten.*
- Point at 60 on the grid, then at – 4 in the subtraction. Ask children to hold up four fingers. Count back along the grid in ones, folding down one finger for each number. *Fifty-nine, fifty-eight, fifty-seven, fifty-six.* Complete the subtraction: *60 – 4 = 56.*
- Write the addition: *56 + 4 = 60. The units add to ten, 4 + 6 = 10. Because we are counting to a multiple of ten, it is as if we are making two numbers make ten.*
- Write *40 – 8 =* □. Alert children's attention to the fact that we are again subtracting from a multiple of ten. Point at '8'. *What matches this number to make ten?* Encourage children to realise it is 2. Point at '40'. *What decade comes before 40?* Write *32* to complete the subtraction.
- Check the answer by counting back eight from 40. *Do we reach the same answer?*
- Repeat the process to subtract 3 from 70 and 9 from 30. Use bonds to ten to help. Stress we do not need to count back.

Activities:

Independent task: Provide each child with PCM 84. Each discusses with a partner but completes a sheet of their own.

Teacher-monitored task: Give each child in a group of eight children a 1–100 number grid. Each chooses a different multiple of ten and writes it. Throw a dice. Children subtract the number thrown from their multiple of ten. Encourage them to use knowledge of pairs that make 10. They write answers. Compare the answers. *They all end in the same units*. Repeat six times.

Assessment criteria:

- Subtract a 1-digit number from a multiple of ten without counting back
- Know pairs of numbers that make ten

Plenary:

Write *34 +* □ *= 50* on board. Ask children to work in pairs to calculate.

Y2 Review of pre-requisite skills for Block D3.a and D3.b

Objectives:

- Add to a multiple of ten and subtract units from a 2-digit number using knowledge of place value
- Count on in ones and 10s

Mental oral starter:

Units on and off

Draw a grid with two rows and four columns. Children copy into their books. Write a 2-digit number in the top left space. Children must subtract units and write the remaining multiple of ten in the matching space on their grid. Continue along the top row. On the bottom row, write a multiple of ten. Throw the dice and ask children to add the dice number to the multiple and write the total in the matching space on their grid. Continue along the bottom row. Check their answers, going along each row with them.

Teaching sequence:

- Show children a 1–100 grid. Choose a number, for example, 47. Ask children to say the number. *Forty-seven.*
- Draw a cross around the number on the grid, outlining two numbers above, two to left, two to right and two below.
- Point at each arm of the cross and discuss with children. *To the left of the number we count back in ones. 47, 46, 45. To the right of the number, we count on in ones: 48, 49. Above the number, we count back in 10s: 37, 27. Below the number, we count on in 10s: 57, 67.*
- Draw an empty cross on the board. Write *63* in the middle. Ask children to discuss the numbers they think will go to the left. *We should count back in ones: 62, 61*. Point at right arm of cross. *What numbers will go to the right of the number?* Give children a moment to consider. *We should count on in ones: 64, 65.*
- Point at the arm of the cross above number 63. *What numbers will go here?* Give children time to consider. *We must count back in 10s: 53, 43*. Point at arm of cross below number. Give children time to think. *We are counting on in 10s: 73, 83.*
- Repeat, drawing a cross with 35 in middle.

Activities:

Independent task: Give each child a copy of PCM 36 to complete individually, then make up few of their own in the same mode.

Teacher-monitored task: Meanwhile, sit a group of eight children at a table. Each child chooses a 2-digit number and writes on the whiteboard. They draw a cross round the number and write numbers one and two less, then one and two more. They write numbers ten and twenty less, and ten and twenty more. When correct, children clean boards and repeat with a new number.

Assessment criteria:

- Understand that if we subtract units from 2-digit number, we are left with multiple of ten
- Count on and back in tens from 2-digit number
- Count on and back in ones from 2-digit number

Plenary:

Write 116 on board. *How many must we count back to be left with 99?* Children talk to a partner and feed back. Repeat, writing *123*.

Y2 Review of pre-requisite skills for Block D3.c and D3.d

Objectives:

- Tell the time at o'clock times on digital and analogue clocks
- Understand each o'clock time occurs twice each 24-hour day

Mental oral starter:

What's the time?

In pairs, children discuss different times of the day and decide which they like best, for example, teatime, bedtime, getting up time, lunchtime. Show an analogue clock, for example, 4 o'clock. Discuss which time of the day this is – for example, teatime. Which pairs have identified this time? Repeat for different o'clock times.

Teaching sequence:

- Show children an analogue clock showing 12 o'clock. Discuss what time this shows. Talk about what we are doing at this time: eating our lunch at midday, sleeping at midnight. Write midday and midnight on the board.
- Show children a digital clock with 12:00 on it. *This time is the same as that shown on the clock-face*. Remind children that the clock shows this time twice a day – once in the middle of the night, once in the middle of the day.
- Show children an analogue clock showing 3 o'clock. Discuss what time this shows. Talk about what we are doing at this time: playing in the middle of the afternoon, sleeping during the night.
- Show children a digital clock with 3:00 on it. *This time is the same as that shown on the clock face*. Remind children that the clock shows 3 o'clock twice a day – once in the middle of the night, once in the middle of the afternoon.
- Show children an analogue clock showing 7 o'clock. Discuss what time this shows. Talk about what we are doing at this time: getting ready for bed at night, waking up in the morning.
- Show children a digital clock with 7:00 on it. *This time is the same as that shown on the clock face*. Remind children that the clock shows this time twice a day – once in the evening, once in the early morning.
- Repeat to show 10 o'clock.

Activities:

Independent task: Give each child a copy of PCM R12. They work with a partner but complete their own sheet.

Teacher-monitored task: Give each child in a group of eight children a sheet of clock-faces (PCM 116). Show children a digital clock time, for example, 4:00. They draw hands on the first of the clock-faces to show the matching time. Check all have done this correctly. *What might we be doing at these two times?* (sleeping in the middle of the night, eating tea during the afternoon). Repeat at least six times.

Assessment criteria:

- Tell o'clock time on both analogue and digital clocks
- Understand each time occurs twice each 24-hour period

Plenary:

Write *4:30* on the board. What time do children think this is on an analogue clock? Repeat for 12:30 and 6:30.

Y2 Review of pre-requisite skills for Block E3.a and E3.b

Objectives:

- Count in 2s to 20 and back
- Count in 5s to 50 and back
- Count in 10s to 100 and back

Mental oral starter:

Counting in fives

Write *55, 105* and *205* on the board. In pairs, children choose one of these and find out how many fives they need to count to reach it. Give children a few minutes then take feedback, for each number in turn, for example: *We must count 11 fives to reach 55; We must count 21 fives to reach 105; We must count 41 fives to reach 205.*

Teaching sequence:

- Show children a counting stick with 10 divisions. *We can count along this in twos*, pointing at the end of the stick. *What will be the last number we say?* Take suggestions. Count along the stick in twos: *two, four, six*, etc. *Twenty is the last number we say.*
- Point at the mid-point of the stick. *What number is this when we count in twos? Ten.* Write *5 × 2 = 10* and point out the fact that if we count five twos, we reach ten. Match five to the fifth place on the stick, and repeat: *five twos are ten*. Point at a different place on the stick. *What number is this when we count in twos?* Record this as multiplication, for example, *8 × 2 = 16.*
- Show the stick to children. *Using this same stick we are going to count in fives*. Point at the end of the stick. *What will be the last number we say?* Take suggestions. Count along the stick in fives: *five, ten, fifteen,* etc. *Fifty is the last number we say.*
- Point at the mid-point of the stick. *What number is this when we count in fives? Twenty-five*. Record as 5 × 5 = 25. *Five fives are twenty-five*. Point at a different place on the stick. *What number is this when we count in fives?* Record the answer as multiplication, for example, *3 × 5 = 15.*
- Repeat, using the stick to count in 10s from 0 and identifying different places on the stick in the 10s count. Record these as multiplications, for example, *7 × 10 = 70.*
- Write 22 on the board. *How many twos must we count to reach this number?* Encourage children to try. Demonstrate that it is eleven: 11 × 2 = 22. Repeat. *How many fives must we count to reach 45? How many 10s to reach 110?*

Activities:

Individual task: Give each child PCM 27 to complete individually.

Teacher-monitored task: Divide six children into pairs. Ask the first pair to count in twos, the second pair in 10s, the third pair in fives. Give each pair a blank track with twelve spaces. Use cards 2–12. Show a card, for example 7. Each pair counts seven of their number and writes the answer in the seventh space on the track. Pairs show the other children. *Are they correct?* Repeat until all cards are used.

Assessment criteria:

- Can count in 2s to 20 and beyond and say how many 2s make a given multiple of 2
- Can count in 5s to 50 and beyond and say how many 5s make a given multiple of 5
- Can count in 10s to 100 and beyond and say how many 10s make a given multiple of 10

Plenary:

Write □ × *5* + □ = *42* on the flipchart. Children work in pairs to discover the missing numbers. Stress that there is more than one correct answer.

Y2 Review of pre-requisite skills for Block E3.c and E3.d

Objectives:

- Double numbers up to 15
- Halve even numbers up to 30

Mental oral starter:

Double or quit …

Children work in pairs to write four even numbers between 2 and 12 on their whiteboards and circle each. Throw a dice. Ask the children to double the number thrown, for example, if the dice lands on 3, double 3 to get 6. If a pair has this number on their whiteboard, they cross it off. Continue. The first pair to cross off all their numbers wins. Bingo!

Teaching sequence:

- Rehearse with children doubling numbers from 1 to 5 using fingers. Demonstrate each double and record it on the board: *1 + 1 = 2, 2 + 2 = 4, 3 + 3 = 6, 4 + 4 = 8, 5 + 5 = 10.*
- Show large 5p and 1p coins. *How much have we here? Six pence. What is double six pence?* Add other 5p and 1p coins below the first ones. Point at two 5p coins. *We have ten pence (double 5p).* Point at two 1p coins. *We have two pence (double 1p). That is twelve pence. Double 6p = 12p.*
- Show large 5p and 2p coins. *How much is this? Seven pence.* Ask children to predict double seven pence. Show two more coins and demonstrate that double seven is ten and four, making fourteen pence. *Double 7p is 14p.*
- Repeat, using 5p, 2p and 1p to show double 8p.
- Show double 5p, 2p, 2p to demonstrate double 9p = 18p.
- Show a 10p coin. *What is double ten pence?* Demonstrate this is 20p.
- Write doubles of numbers 6–10 on board. *6 + 6 = 12, 7 + 7 = 14, 8 + 8 = 16, 9 + 9 = 18, 10 + 10 = 20.* Rehearse together.
- Write *14* on board. *What is half of fourteen?* Point at the relevant double: *7 + 7 = 14. Double seven is fourteen so half of fourteen is seven.*
- Repeat to find half of 18 and 12.
- Write 13p on the board. Ask children if they can work out double 13. Show that we can double 10p (20p) then add double 3p (6p) to get 26p. Repeat to double 15p.

Activities:

Independent task: Give each child a copy of PCM 29 each. Children work with a partner. Any who finish try PCM 30.

Teacher-monitored task: Meanwhile, sit a group of six children at a table. You need 1p, 2p, 5p and 10p coins. Give each child an amount between 2p and 15p. They work out how much they have, then double and write the total. Check each answer, if necessary using coins. Give each child a new handful of coins to double. Extend some children beyond 15p if appropriate.

Assessment criteria:

- Double numbers 1–15 inclusive
- Halve even numbers to 30

Plenary:

Write *£4.50* on the board. Ask children to suggest different ways of making this amount using doubling and adding (e.g. double £2 and add 50p).

Introduction to the Tests

The tests are designed to provide a raft of useful information about the sub-level at which each child is operating. How effective the tests are at predicting this depends very much on *how* they are used. Please read carefully the information below.

Tips for best use

- The *Abacus Evolve* End-of-term Tests help you to gather evidence to support your own professional understanding of each child's level of achievement. The tests on their own do not determine this.

> That's interesting. Sunil has done better than I anticipated in the test. I must look again at my evidence before deciding on a sub-level.

> This is useful: the test confirms that Tara is right in the centre of sub-level 3c. That is good to know.

- Each test allows children to demonstrate achievement across a relatively limited range of National Curriculum sub-levels. Therefore each test is only useful for children who are anticipated to reach the sub-levels within this range.
- Children in your class who are not expected to achieve, or who are expected to achieve beyond, the sub-levels within the range of the test can be given one of the following.
    - The *Abacus Evolve* End-of-term Test from the previous term. This will allow them to demonstrate achievement within a range of slightly lower sub-levels.

    > I will give all the children in my lowest ability group the Spring test rather than the Summer one. That will help to give me a realistic picture of how far they have progressed.

    - The *Abacus Evolve* End-of-term Test B. These are specifically designed to allow children to demonstrate achievement at a slightly higher level.

    > Umesh, Jessie, Kolina, Connor and Richard need extending. Perhaps they can have a go at Test B.

    - Teacher-generated assessments, designed specifically with that child in mind and targeted at their specific learning goals.

    > I've used the test from the previous year to help me design a special test for Beatrice. That will mean she is not left out, and it will also give me some more evidence of her level of operation.

- *Abacus Evolve* tests are provided each term. It is inadvisable to attempt to assess the sub-level at which a child is operating more frequently than this. *Abacus Evolve* Half-term Tests may be used to augment ongoing teacher assessment.

> This Overview Sheet is so useful! Looking at the scores from the Half-term Tests and my own teacher assessments, I can tell which *Abacus Evolve* End-of-term Test to give to each child.

- All this information may be collated on the Class Overview Sheet. You can use this information to identify common strengths and weaknesses throughout the class to inform your future plans.

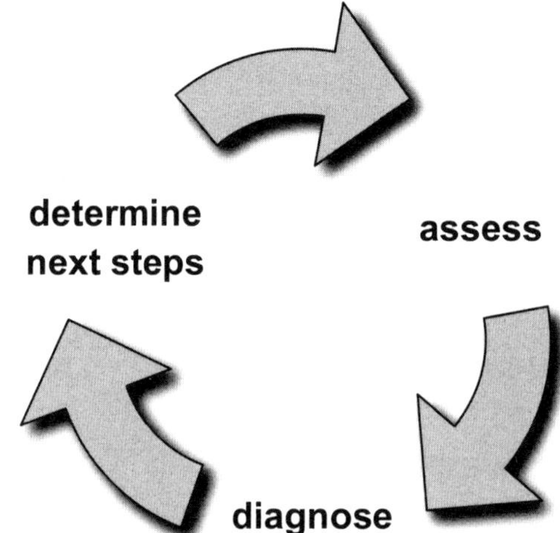

Children need to be continuously assessed so that you can diagnose any difficulties and decide what to do next. Use the diagnostic information provided with the tests to help you with this process.

Don’t forget...

☑ Check the range of sub-levels anticipated by the test (see end of this *Assessment Kit*).
☑ Do not rely solely on test information to identify a sub-level.
☑ Collate all relevant information on the Class Overview Sheet.

About the Mental Tests

The following tests consist of two parts:

- **scripts** from which you can read out the questions to the children
- **pupil answer sheets**.

There are accompanying **Test Information and commentary charts** (containing *answers* to test questions, identifying the *objectives* being tested, and providing a *diagnostic commentary* for each question, highlighting common errors).

There are also **Class achievement record** sheets. These sheets list all the objectives tested in a grid format so you can record individual children's achievement against the objectives according to their performance in the test. They can be found towards the end of this *Assessment Kit*, pages 140–142.

The test assumes that the 'default' ***Abacus Evolve*** sequence of blocks has been followed throughout the year to this point. The tests therefore contain questions relating to any of the Blocks A1–E1 (autumn), Blocks A2–E2 (spring), Blocks A3–E3 (summer).

If you have not taught some of these blocks, we suggest you check the **Test information and commentary charts** to ensure that all questions relate to the teaching you have done.

Teacher's script

Read each question aloud once, allow children approximately 3 seconds to consider, then repeat the question. Allow another interval of 10 seconds or so before moving on to the next question.

Number	Question
	I'm going to read out some questions to you, which I want you to answer on the pupil sheet in front of you. I will ask each question twice so you have time to answer it. At the end of the questions you will be allowed to draw a picture of a car.
1	Write 24 in figures.
2	Add 4 and 6.
3	What is double 5?
4	Mary has 5p. She gets 10p from her mum and 10p from her gran. How much has she now?
5	What is the sum of 3 add 2 add 7?
6	Look at your answer sheet. Ring the pentagon.
7	Look at the number on your answer sheet. Put a ring around the tens digit.
8	Look at the answer sheet. How many centimetres long is the crayon?
9	What is one-half of 20?
10	Look at the four numbers on your answer sheet. Put a ring around the largest number.
	Now turn over your sheet and draw a car.

Year 2 Autumn • Mental

Pupil sheet

Name ....

1		
2		4 6
3		
4	p	5p 10p 10p
5		3 2 7
6		
7	58	
8	cm	0 10cm
9		
10	32 29 46 57	

Test information and commentary chart

Q. no.	Objective	Block	Answer	Common difficulties and advice
1	Read and write numbers up to 100 in figures	A1	24	Some children write 204, which is the literal translation of 'twenty-four'. Remind such children about the place value grid and how to write the 2-digit answer to 20 + 4.
2	Rehearse addition and subtraction facts for pairs of numbers that total 10	B1	10	Some try to count on 6 from 4 and include 4 in the count, writing 9 as the answer. The answer to 4 + 6 should be a memorised addition fact.
3	Know by heart doubles for numbers up to at least 15 and corresponding halves	E1	10	Only those who do not understand the idea of 'double' get this incorrect. Remind them of the relationship between double 5 and 5 + 5.
4	Solve 'real-life' problems involving money (paying an exact sum)	E1	25p	Although the addition 5p + 10p + 10p would be easy for most Year 2 children if in a written format, the oral approach, together with the time limit, causes some children difficulties. Remind them that the amounts to be added are in the hints box of their answer sheet.
5	Add three numbers by putting the largest number first	B1	12	Although the numbers 3, 2 and 7 are in the hint box, many children do not change the order to 3, 7 and 2 – finding a pair that makes 10. Children's response to the oral presentation is different to a written one and dominates their thinking. Thus children end by adding 5 and 7, some writing 11 as they include the 5 in the count on 7.
6	Use the names of common 2D shapes, including: pentagon, hexagon, octagon	D1	3rd shape	This question is about knowledge and children either know the correct answer or do not. You may wish to set up a matching activity on a shapes table, with polygons and their names on card.
7	Know what each digit in a 2-digit number represents, including 0 as a place holder	A1	(5) 8	It is worth checking with some children that they did not ring 5 by guessing as there are only two digits to choose from and 5 is the first.
8	Estimate, measure and compare lengths using standard units: centimetres and metres	C1	5cm	Because of the position of the start of the pencil at the 2cm mark, many children will write 7cm as the answer. Talk those who write this as they are likely to meet similar questions again.
9	Begin to halve multiples of 10 up to 100	E1	10	The small minority who get this wrong do not understand the idea of 'one-half' of a number. Make a rod 20 cubes long and show them how many cubes are in one-half of the rod when you break it into two halves.
10	Order numbers up to at least 100	A1	57	29 is sometimes written as the answer. Here children are choosing the number with the largest units digit. Use a number line or 100 number square to show the relative positions of the four numbers. Remind them that the tens digits should be the first to be compared and then the unit digits only when the tens digits are the same.

Teacher's script

Read each question aloud once, allow children approximately 3 seconds to consider, then repeat the question. Allow another interval of 10 seconds or so before moving on to the next question.

Number	Question
	I'm going to read out some questions to you, which I want you to answer on the pupil sheet in front of you. I will ask each question twice so you have time to answer it. At the end of the questions you will be allowed to draw a garden.
1	What is the difference between 10 and 7?
2	Look at the sequence on your sheet. Write in the next number in the sequence.
3	Take 20 away from 52.
4	What is 10 more than 54?
5	Count on two hundreds from 500. What number did you get to?
6	Look at your sheet. Put a ring around the even number.
7	A bag holds ten oranges. How many oranges are there altogether in four bags?
8	What number comes between 79 and 81?
9	How many sets of four make 20?
10	What is 17 add 9?
	Now turn over your sheet and draw a garden.

Pupil sheet

Name ....

1		10 7
2	38 40 42 ☐	
3		20 52
4		54
5		
6	27 31 28 43	
7		10
8		79 81
9		
10		

Year 2 Spring • Mental

Test information and commentary chart

Q. no.	Objective	Block	Answer	Common difficulties and advice
1	Rehearse addition and subtraction facts for pairs of numbers that total up to 10	B2	3	A common error is 4. Children who count back from 10 may say 10, 9, 8, 7 and write 4. Those that count on may say 7, 8, 9, 10 and write 4.
2	Count on in 2s, 5s or 10s up to 100	E2	44	43 is written as the next number after 44.
3	Subtract a multiple of 10 from a 2-digit number by counting back in 10s	D2	32	30 as two tens are taken away from the tens digit 5, leaving 50.
4	Count on or back in 1s from a 2-digit number	A2	64	60 as children count on 1 ten from the 5 tens and forget about the 4 units.
5	Count on and back in 100s from a multiple of 100	A2	700	300 as children count back 200 from 500. Some count on in 1s and get lost.
6	Begin to recognise odd and even numbers up to at least 50	A2	28	43 as the tens digit, 4, is larger than the units digit, 3, and is even.
7	Introduce multiplication as 'lots of'	E2	40	14 with children adding the 10 and 4.
8	Say a number lying between two numbers, up to at least 100	A2	80	Numbers less than 79 as 'between' is interpreted as meaning 'less than both numbers'.
9	Begin to understand division as grouping	E2	5	24 as 4 is added to 20.
10	Add and subtract 9 and 11 by adding and subtracting 10	E2	26	Children are expected to use the strategy of adding 10 and then subtracting 1. If they attempt to count on 9, errors are likely.

Teacher's script

Read each question aloud once, allow children approximately 3 seconds to consider, then repeat the question. Allow another interval of 10 seconds or so before moving on to the next question.

Number	Question
	I'm going to read out some questions to you, which I want you to answer on the pupil sheet in front of you. I will ask each question twice so you have time to answer it. At the end of the questions you will be allowed to draw a picture of summer.
1	What is the difference between 37 and 34?
2	What is the sum of 30 and 70?
3	Look at the jug on your sheet. How many litres of water are in the jug?
4	What is 5 multiplied by 6?
5	Sam has 18 stickers. He gives half of them to Tom. How many stickers has Sam left?
6	Look at the number on your answer sheet. What is the hundreds digit?
7	What is double 35?
8	Aisha has three 10p coins. How much money has Aisha altogether?
9	What is 36 rounded to the nearest ten?
10	A cake is cut into four equal pieces. What fraction of the whole cake is one piece?
	Now turn over your sheet and draw a picture of summer.

Year 2 Summer • Mental

Pupil sheet

Name ....

1		37 34
2		
3	l	4l 2l
4		
5		18
6		436
7		
8		
9		36
10		

Test information and commentary chart

Q. no.	Objective	Block	Answer	Common difficulties and advice
1	Find the difference between two numbers by counting on	A3	3	4 as counting includes 34, 35, 36, 37, which is four numbers. 2 as there are two numbers, 35 and 36 between 37 and 34.
2	Know by heart pairs of multiples of 10 that total 100	B3	100	80 or 90 as errors are made in the counting on of 70 from 30.
3	Read a simple capacity scale to the nearest labelled and unlabelled division	C3	3 litres	$2\frac{1}{2}$ litres as the mark is halfway from 2 to the next labelled mark.
4	Know by heart the multiplication facts for 2, 5 and 10 times-tables	E3	30	11 as it is easier to add than multiply.
5	Begin to recognise halves and quarters of small numbers of objects	E3	9	10, as half of 18 is calculated as 8 leaving Sam with 10.
6	Begin to partition 3-digit numbers into H, T and U	A3	4	3 or 6 as place value is not yet understood.
7	Double multiples of 5 up to 50	E3	70	610 as double 3 is 6 and double 5 is 10.
8	Begin to understand multiplication as repeated addition or as describing an array	E3	30p	13p as 3 + 10p = 13p.
9	Begin to round numbers less than 100 to the nearest 10	A3	40	46 as 10 is added to 36.
10	Begin to recognise halves and quarters of small numbers of objects	B3	$\frac{1}{4}$ *or* a quarter *or* one-quarter	$\frac{1}{2}$ as this is the most well-known fraction.

About the Half-term Written Tests

There are two half-term written tests for each term:

- **part A** is pitched at a level appropriate to all of the children in the class (except very low achievers)
- **part B** is written at an extension level; you may wish to give this selectively to higher achievers, possibly at a different time.

For each test there is an accompanying **Test Information and commentary chart** (containing *answers* to test questions, identifying the *objectives* being tested, and a *diagnostic commentary* for each question, highlighting common errors and how these may be addressed).

For each test there is also a **Class achievement record** sheet. This sheet lists all the objectives tested in a grid format so you can record individual children's achievement against the objectives according to their performance in the test. They can be found towards the end of this *Assessment Kit*, pages 143–148.

All the tests have been created using the 'default' ***Abacus Evolve*** sequence of blocks for each half-term: Blocks A1–B1 for the Autumn Half-term Tests, Blocks A2–B2 for the Spring Half-term Tests and Blocks A3–B3 for the Summer Half-term Tests.

If you have not taught some of these blocks, we suggest you check the **Test information and commentary charts** for each of Tests A and B to ensure that all questions relate to the teaching you have done.

Year 2 Autumn half-term • Written A

Name ....

1. Write the **missing** numbers.

   a) sixty ↔ ☐ b) sixteen ↔ ☐

2. Count **on** in **tens**.

   27 → ☐ → ☐ → ☐ → ☐ → ☐ → ☐ → ☐

3. How many sheep **altogether**? ☐

4. Write how much **money** is in each set.

   a) ☐ 10 10 1 10 10 1 b) ☐ 10 10 1 1 10 1 1 1

   Coin labels: TEN PENCE, ONE PENNY

5. Write down these numbers in **order**, from smallest to largest.

   a) **32, 43, 16** b) **75, 83, 38, 77**

   ☐ ☐ ☐ ☐ ☐ ☐ ☐

6 Work out the answers.

a) **14 + 3 =** ☐ b) **68 + 7 =** ☐

7 Write in the **missing** numbers.

a) **3 +** ☐ **= 6** b) ☐ **+ 3 = 7**

c) **2 +** ☐ **= 8** d) ☐ **+ 2 = 9**

8 Work out the answers.

a) **6 – 1 =** ☐ b) **8 – 4 =** ☐

9 Work out the answers.

a) **5 + 2 =** ☐ b) **3 + 5 =** ☐

Year 2 Autumn half-term • Written A

Test information and commentary chart

Q. no.	Objective	Block	Answer	Common difficulties and advice
1a	Read and write numbers up to 100 in figures	A1	60	A very small number of children will write 6 as the answer. Use number name cards 'six' and 'sixty', together with number cards 6 and 60, to encourage children to match the correct pairs. Discuss the differences between each number and the number names.
1b	Read and write numbers up to 100 in figures	A1	16	Look for those who write '61'. Distinguish between those who reverse many 2-digit numbers and those who translate 'sixteen' literally as 'six' and 'teen', writing '6' followed by '1'. The latter need more work with place value and matching names with numbers. Discuss with them the lack of match between the way we say and write the 'teen' numbers.
2	Count on and back in 1s or 10s from a 2-digit number	A1	27, 37, 47, 57, 67, 77, 87, 97	An unusual error is to write 30, 37, 40, 47, 50, 57, 60. Here the child has interpreted 'count on in tens' as 'count to the next ten'. Some children will count on in ones. Stress the need to read the question carefully, particularly the words in bold.
3	Begin to count up to 100 objects by grouping in 5s or 10s	A1	43	Some children count in ones, ignoring the sets of 10. Draw their attention to the sets and practise counting in 10s, adding the three separate sheep.
4a, b	Partition 2-digit numbers into T and U	A1	a) 42p b) 35p	Check that children are separating the 10p coins from the 1p coins when counting. This will lead to the correct placement of the digits in the two-digit number.
5a, b	Order numbers up to at least 100 and position them on a 100-square	A1	a) 16, 32, 43 b) 38, 75, 77, 83	Make sure children appreciate that positioning the tens is all important. If they have difficulty, refer them to a 100-square.
6a	Add by counting on in 1s from the larger number, crossing a multiple of 10	B1	17	A few children will write 16 as the answer, counting 14 as part of the count on 3, i.e. 14, 15, 16, giving 16 as their answer. Show them how a number line emphasises that it is the jumps that are counted, not the numbers. 1 1 1 14 15 16 17
6b	Add by counting on in 1s from the larger number, crossing a multiple of 10	B1	75	Incorrect answers such as 74 and 76 indicate counting on errors. Remind children that partitioning breaks down the addition into manageable parts, i.e. 68 + 7 = 68 + 2 + 5 = 70 + 5 = 75.

Q. no.	Objective	Block	Answer	Common difficulties and advice
7a	Rehearse addition and subtraction facts for pairs of numbers that total up to 9	B1	3	The incorrect answer 2 is not infrequent. Here children count the numbers between 3 and 6, i.e. 4 and 5 (two numbers, hence 2). 9 is also common, with children adding 3 and 6 as they respond to the missing number format by seeing the addition sign and the two numbers 3 and 6 – hence 3 + 6 = 9. Use a number line to show the missing jumps. 1 1 1 3 4 5 6
7b	Rehearse addition and subtraction facts for pairs of numbers that total up to 9	B1	4	Some count how many numbers there are between 3 and 7, i.e. 4, 5, 6 (three numbers), writing the answer 3. You may wish to remind them of the match (equivalence) between the addition ? + 3 = 7 and the subtraction ? = 7 – 3. A number line shows this well. 1 1 1 1 3 4 5 6 7
7c	Rehearse addition and subtraction facts for pairs of numbers that total up to 9	B1	6	The incorrect answer 5 is not infrequent. Here children count the numbers between 2 and 8, i.e. 3, 4, 5, 6 and 7 (five numbers, hence 5). 10 is also common, with children adding 2 and 8 as they respond to the missing number format by seeing the addition sign and the two numbers 2 and 8 – hence 2 + 8 = 10. Use a number line to show the missing jumps. 1 1 1 1 1 1 2 3 4 5 6 7 8
7d	Rehearse addition and subtraction facts for pairs of numbers that total up to 9	B1	7	Some count how many numbers there are between 2 and 9, i.e. 3, 4, 5, 6, 7, 8 7 (six numbers), writing the answer 6. You may wish to remind them of the match (equivalence) between the addition ? + 2 = 9 and the subtraction ? = 9 – 2. A number line shows this well. 1 1 1 1 1 1 1 2 3 4 5 6 7 8 9
8a	Rehearse addition and subtraction facts for pairs of numbers that total up to 9	B1	5	A common error is to add 6 and 1. Children who misread the operation may find flash cards of mixed simple additions and subtractions helpful, particularly if they only read the question aloud without working out the answers.
8b	Rehearse addition and subtraction facts for pairs of numbers that total up to 9	B1	4	A common error is to add 8 and 4. Children who misread the operation may find flash cards of mixed simple additions and subtractions helpful, particularly if they only read the question aloud without working out the answers.

Q. no.	Objective	Block	Answer	Common difficulties and advice
9a	Rehearse addition and subtraction facts for pairs of numbers that total 10	B1	7	6 is an error made by only one or two children. This is often due to children counting on 2 from 5, but including 5 in their count, i.e. 5, 6. Show such children how count on works on a number line with the count on as a jump, not the numbers. 1 1 5 6 7 8
9b	Rehearse addition and subtraction facts for pairs of numbers that total 10	B1	8	The same misconception as with 5 + 2 occurs here, with 7 given as the answer. Look for those who record 3 + 5 as 3 + 4 = 7 + 1 = 8. Although the statements are mathematically incorrect, it shows how a child has used near doubles.

Name ....

1 Each packet has **10** envelopes. There are some single envelopes.

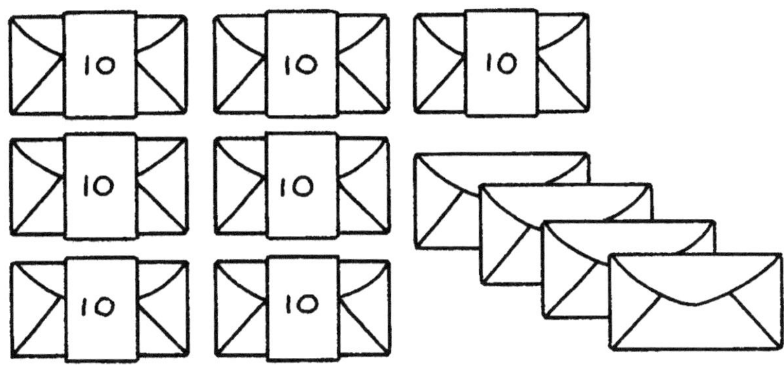

How many envelopes are there **altogether**? 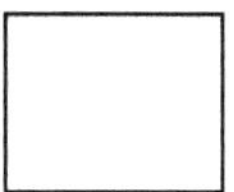

2 Write how much **money** is in each set.

a) b)

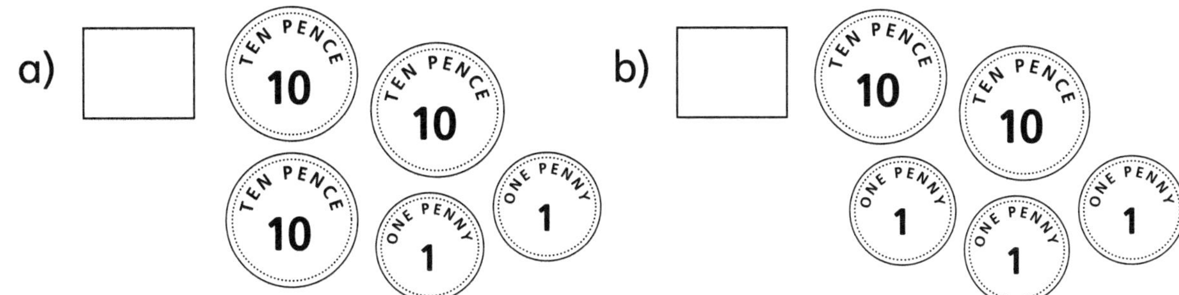

c)

d) What is the **total** of all three sets of coins?

3 If these numbers were put in **order**, what would be the middle number?

a) b)

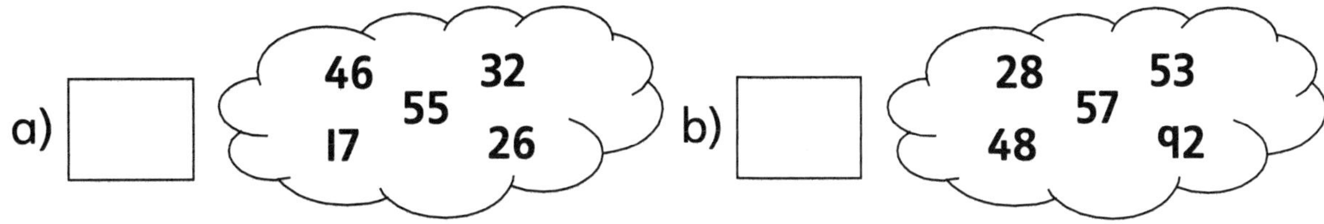

4 The **missing** numbers are both **more than 6**.
Write in what the **missing** numbers could be.

☐ + ☐ = **31**

5 Write in the **missing** numbers.

a) **46 + 8 =** ☐ b) **7 + 84 =** ☐

c) **73 +** ☐ **= 82** d) ☐ **+ 38 = 44**

6 Write in the **missing** numbers.

a) ☐ **+ 8 + 5 = 17** b) **7 + 8 +** ☐ **= 20**

7 What could the **missing pairs** of numbers be?
Make each pair **different**.

☐ + ☐ = **10** ☐ + ☐ = **10**

☐ + ☐ = **10** ☐ + ☐ = **10**

Year 2 Autumn half-term • Written B

Test information and commentary chart

Q. no.	Objective	Block	Answer	Common difficulties and advice
1	Begin to count up to 100 objects by grouping in 5s or 10s	A1	74	Children count only the number of envelopes, giving an answer of 11. Encourage them to read the information and the question, as well as studying the picture.
2a, b, c, d	Partition 2-digit numbers into T and U	A1	a) 32p b) 23p c) 44p d) 99p	Check that children are separating the 10p coins from the 1p coins when counting. This leads to the correct placement of the digits in the two-digit number. The same applies to finding the total.
3a, b	Order numbers up to at least 100 and position them on a 100-square	A1	a) 32 b) 53	Children can locate the middle number by writing them in order first. A very able child might appreciate that the middle number is the third one.
4	Add by counting on in 1s from the larger number, crossing a multiple of 10	B1	Any pair, each number > 6, e.g. 20 + 11	Some children do not apply the constraint that both numbers should be more than 6. There is a tendency by a few to move directly to the 'problem', ignoring the instructions that precede it. Cover up the open addition and encourage children to read the instructions first.
5a	Add by counting on in 1s from the larger number, crossing a multiple of 10	B1	54	Incorrect answers such as 53, 55 and 56 suggest miscounting. Ask those children to work out the addition aloud so you can see where their mistakes occur. You may wish to remind them of partitioning as a method, i.e. 46 + 8 = 46 + 4 + 4 = 50 + 4 = 54.
5b	Add by counting on in 1s from the larger number, crossing a multiple of 10	B1	91	More children get this incorrect than 5a. This is due to the addition being 7 + 84 rather than 84 + 7. Some children do not use the idea of changing the order to add. Many incorrect answers in the 90s result from not using this approach. Ask these children to work aloud to see if they can work it out by changing the order.
5c	Add by counting on in 1s from the larger number, crossing a multiple of 10	B1	9	The answer 10 occurs often when children count on and include 73. As with other similar additions, show them how a number line helps.
5d	Add by counting on in 1s from the larger number, crossing a multiple of 10	B1	6	The incorrect answer 7 is due to either a count on or back error, with 38 or 44 being included in the count. Children who consistently use this method incorrectly should be reminded of another method, such as partitioning.

Q. no.	Objective	Block	Answer	Common difficulties and advice
6a	Add three numbers by putting the largest number first	B1	4	9 is a common error as children who do not understand the idea of a missing number find what added to the 8 makes 17. Show them the missing number on a number line: ? 8 5 0 17 or as three number rods making 17: ? 8 5 17
6b	Add three numbers by putting the largest number first	B1	5	Similarly to 6a, a common error is 15. 6 also occurs which is due to children adding 7 and 8 to get 15, and then counting on to 20 – but including 15 in their count. The same help as in 6a should be provided.
7	Rehearse addition and subtraction facts for pairs of numbers that total up to 10	B1	Any four different pairs that have the sum of 10	Most Year 2 children can successfully write four different pairs that make 10. This is important for later work. For the few who have difficulty, let them use two colours, linking cube rods to make 10 in different ways and recording in a pattern vertically: 10 + 0, 9 + 1, 8 + 2, 7 + 3, 6 + 4, 5 + 5, 4 + 6, 3 + 7, 2 + 8, 1 + 9, 0 + 10. Talk about the pattern with children, particularly why it works.

Name ....

1 Each box holds **100** toothbrushes.

How many toothbrushes are there **altogether**? 

2 Write the numbers that the arrows are **pointing** to.

a) b) c)

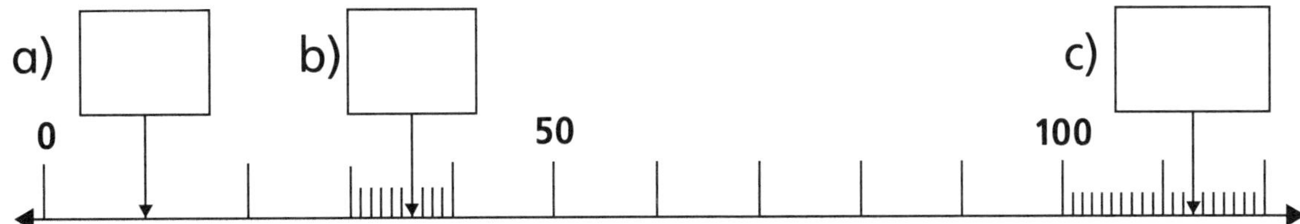

3 This is a **count on in twos** sequence.

Complete the sequence.

4 a) Colour the **even** numbers in the grid.

0	1	2	3	4
5	6	7	8	9
10	11	12	13	14
15	16	17	18	19

b) Colour the **odd** numbers in the grid.

0	1	2	3	4	5
6	7	8	9	10	11
12	13	14	15	16	17
18	19	20	21	22	23

5 Write in the **missing** numbers.

a) 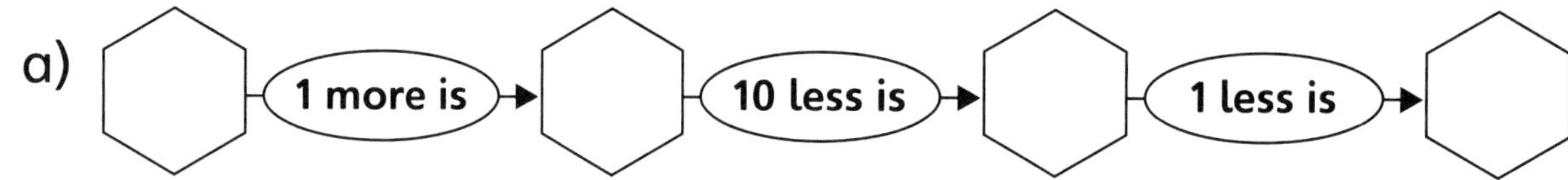

b) 

6 Choose numbers from the television that are:

a) more than **87** ☐

b) less than **20** ☐

c) between **31** and **56** ☐

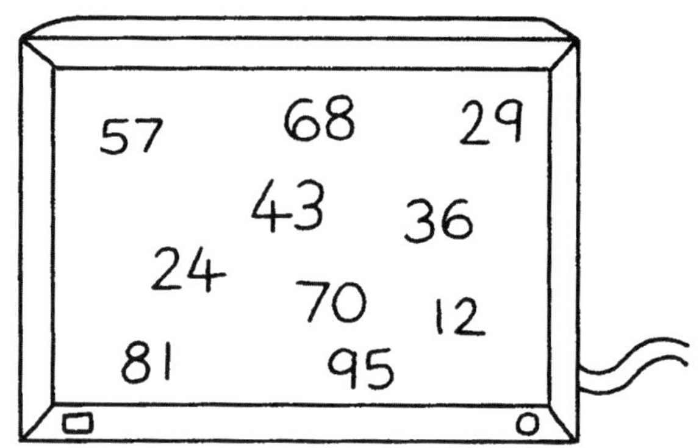

7 Work out the answers.

a) **3** + **6** = ☐ b) **4** + **1** = ☐ c) **0** + **7** = ☐

8 Work out the answers.

a) **6** − **1** = ☐ b) **10** − **7** = ☐ c) **8** − **6** = ☐

9 Tick (✓) the angles that are **more** than a **right angle**.

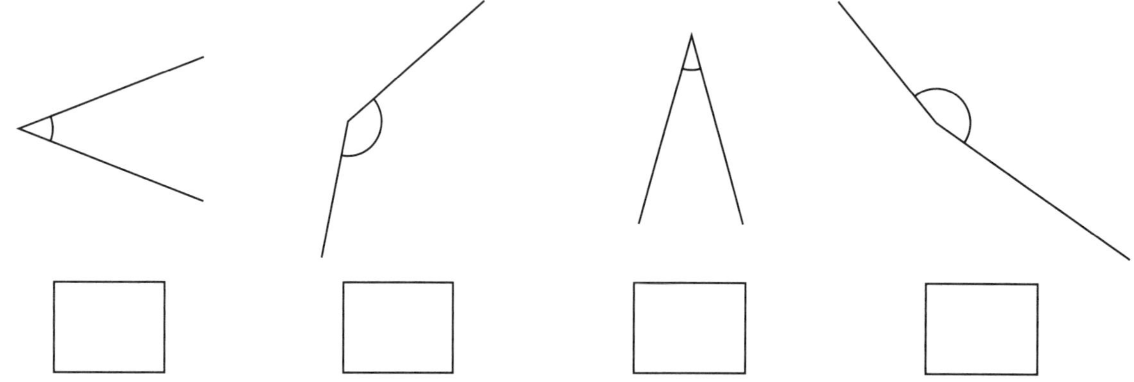

10 Write down the number of **right angles** in each shape.

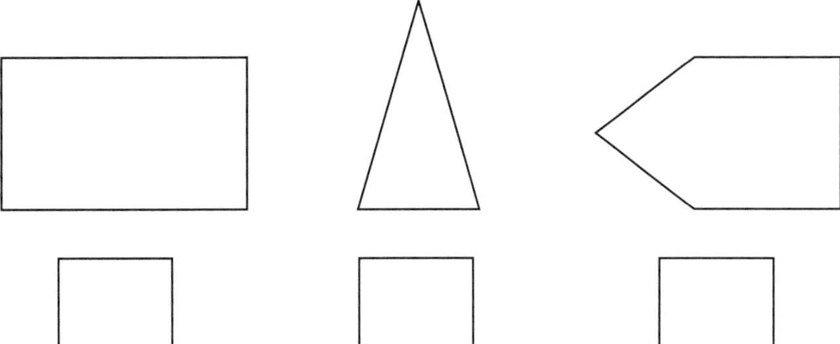

11 Turn each arrow.
Draw each arrow on its new position.

a) $\frac{1}{4}$ turn clockwise

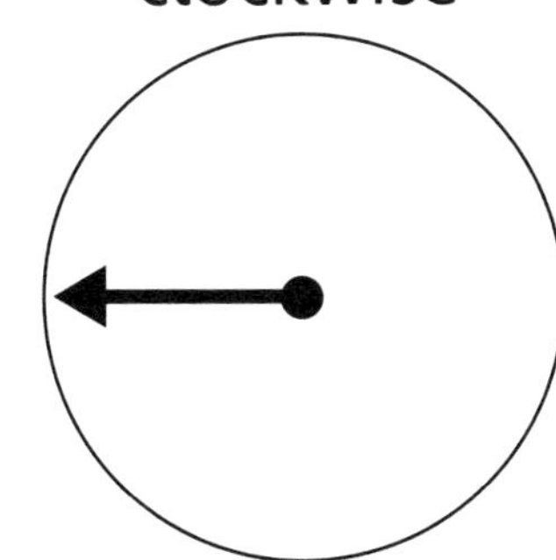

b) 3 right angles anticlockwise

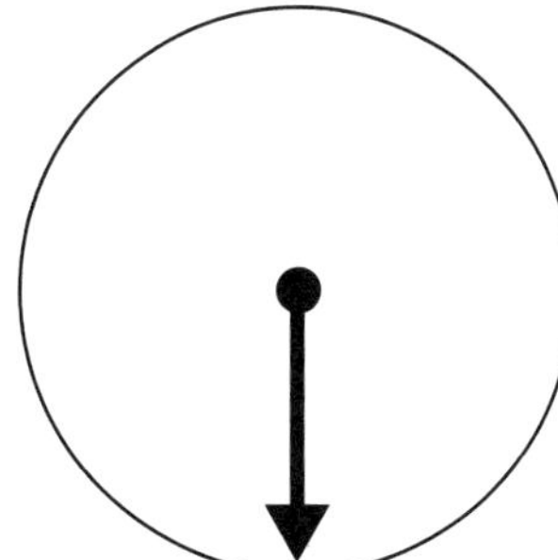

Test information and commentary chart

Q. no.	Objective	Block	Answer	Common difficulties and advice
1	Count on and back in 100s from a multiple of 100	A2	600	A few children either do not understand the information in the first sentence or, more likely, move directly to the picture of the boxes. They proceed to count the boxes or the toothbrushes on the boxes. This results in the answer 6. Talk about the importance of reading the whole question before trying to find the answer.
2a	Count on and back in 1s or 10s from a 2-digit or 3-digit number	A2	10	1 is a common incorrect answer. Children assume that as the previous mark is labeled 0, then the next must be 1. Suggest that they work out the label for every large mark before looking specifically at those for the boxes. This allows them to check that they have the correct sequence.
2b	Count on and back in 1s or 10s from a 2-digit or 3-digit number	A2	36	An answer of 30 is common. Having got 10 correct, children count on to 20 for the next mark and write 30 in the box. Talk with them about the different divisions and what they represent.
2c	Count on and back in 1s or 10s from a 2-digit or 3-digit number	A2	113	Very many children write 101. Having seen 100 at the previous large mark, they write the next number in the counting sequence. The advice in 2b applies here.
3	Count on in 2s (revise)	A2	12, 14, 16, 18, 20, 22, 24, 26, 28, 30	A small minority of children are unable to sustain the use of the 'rule' for a sequence. This is apparent when the first few missing numbers in the sequence are correct and then the rest become the counting numbers. Recommend to children that they write the change (rule) between each number, including the missing numbers. This keeps the rule visible, not only in their 'heads', and where it has to be used. +2 +2 +2 +2 +2 +2 +2 +2 +2 12 14 16 □ □ □ □ □ □ □
4a	Begin to recognise odd and even numbers up to at least 50	A2	**0** 1 **2** 3 **4** 5 **6** 7 **8** 9 **10** 11 **12** 13 **14** 15 **16** 17 **18** 19	At this early stage even numbers are 'understood' through their counting pattern, 2, 4, 6... This reveals itself on number grids. Some children fail to recognise that zero belongs to this pattern. Talk with children about zero as belonging to the pattern.
4b	Begin to recognise odd and even numbers up to at least 50	A2	0 **1** 2 **3** 4 **5** 6 **7** 8 **9** 10 **11** 12 **13** 14 **15** 16 **17** 18 **19** 20 **21** 22 **23**	Odd numbers are less well known than even numbers at this early stage of development. Some children believe that a whole number can be both even and odd. Zero is a particular example of this, but it also applies to other numbers. Do not be misled by those who correctly recognise small numbers as even or odd. Larger numbers behave differently, so some children believe.

Q. no.	Objective	Block	Answer	Common difficulties and advice
5a	Count on and back in 1s or 10s from a 2-digit or 3-digit number	A2	17, 18, 8, 7	Few children fail to get the 18 correct. Some then proceed to find 10 more than 18 rather than 10 less. Others, seeing that the first two numbers are 17 and 18, proceed to write 19 and 20 for the next numbers, ignoring the operations. Advise them to cover up all but two numbers and the operation.
5b	Count on and back in 1s or 10s from a 2-digit or 3-digit number	A2	49, 59, 60, 50	50 is a common error for 59 with children working out 1 more rather than 10 more. Remind children to read all parts of the question before working out the answer to each part. This contrasts the different sections. When they begin again they are more likely to read and follow instructions correctly.
6a	Compare two or more 2-digit numbers	A2	95	Children who get this incorrect usually make up an answer that is not in the television. Check to see if, however, they have chosen a number that is more than 87.
6b	Compare two or more 2-digit numbers	A2	12	'Less than' causes low achievers some difficulties, particularly when they have to choose from a given set. 29 is a common error. Show them a number track, line or grid and talk about relative positions of pairs of numbers.
6c	Say a number lying between two numbers, up to at least 100	A2	36 or 43	24 is a common error. This is less than both 31 and 56, which is how children interpret 'between' when not having total understanding. Again a number line or track is helpful.
7a, b, c	Rehearse addition and subtraction facts for pairs of numbers that total up to 10	B2	a) 9 b) 5 c) 7	Only a very few children are unable to get these three additions correct. For those who have difficulty, the match between symbolism and real objects such as linking cubes, or pictures such as number tracks or lines, needs to be reinforced.
8a	Rehearse addition and subtraction facts for pairs of numbers that total up to 10	B2	5	Subtracting 1 from any whole number is very easy for the vast majority of children.

Q. no.	Objective	Block	Answer	Common difficulties and advice
8b	Rehearse addition and subtraction facts for pairs of numbers that total up to 10	B2	3	4 is a common error. Here children count on from 7 to 10, including 7 in their count. 2 also occurs. This is due to children counting only those numbers between 7 and 10, i.e. 8 and 9 (two numbers). It is essential that these misunderstandings are corrected quickly. The number line is helpful and should be available to all children to be used when needed. Remind children that it is the jumps that are counted, not the numbers. 3 1 1 1 7 8 9 10
8c	Rehearse addition and subtraction facts for pairs of numbers that total up to 10	B2	2	3 and 1 are common errors for the same reasons as 4 and 2 in question 8b. The same advice should be followed.
9	Know that a right-angle is a measure of a quarter turn	B2	The second and fourth boxes should be ticked.	This question requires children to appreciate that right-angles can be in different orientations. For those who have difficulty, emphasise the concept of turning from one arm of the angle to the other – these can then be checked with a right-angle tester.
10	Recognise right angles in simple shapes	B2	Rectangle: 4 Triangle: 0 Irregular Pentagon: 2	Some children may have difficulty recognising all the angles of a shape. Direct them to the vertices, and an appreciation that each polygon has a number of angles to match the number of vertices.
11a	Recognise whole, half and quarter turns; recognise clockwise and anticlockwise turns	B2	$\frac{1}{4}$ turn clockwise	Some children are confused between clockwise and anticlockwise. As these directions of turn are a convention, they must be reminded of the differences as frequently as possible.
11b	Recognise clockwise and anticlockwise turns; know that a right angle is a measure of a quarter turn	B2	3 right angles anticlockwise	Those who do not understand right angle as a turn draw the arrow in a random position. Children need to have practical experiences turning arrows in both directions and by different amounts.

Year 2 Spring half-term • Written B

Name ....

1 Write in the **missing** numbers.

2 Tick (✓) the correct box for each number.
One has been done for you.

number	is an even number	is an odd number	is both even and odd	is neither even nor odd
6				
77				
994				
51				
100				

3 Deidre has **124** stickers. Vinnie has **10 less** than Deidre **and 1 more** than Imran. Jelena has **10 more** than Imran. Write how many stickers each has.

Deidre	Vinnie	Imran	Jelena

4 The four 2-digit numbers are in **order**, smallest first. Write what the **missing** digits could be.

☐ 9	☐ 8	☐ 7	4 ☐

smallest ⟶ largest

5 Write in the **missing** numbers.

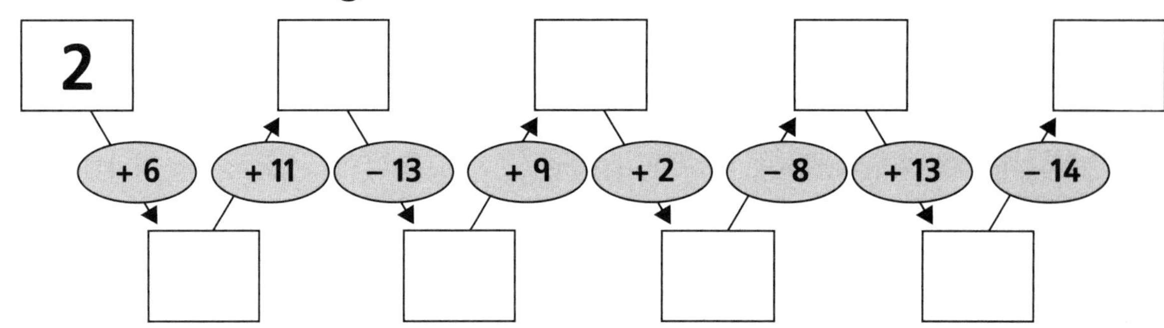

6 Write the number of **right angles** each arrow has **turned**.

a) clockwise

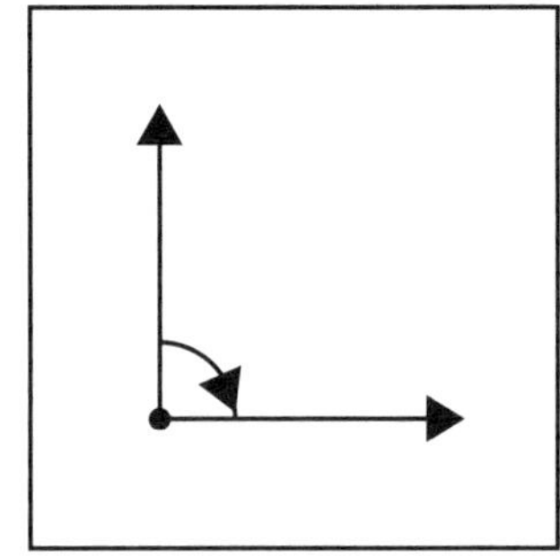

☐ right angles

b) anticlockwise

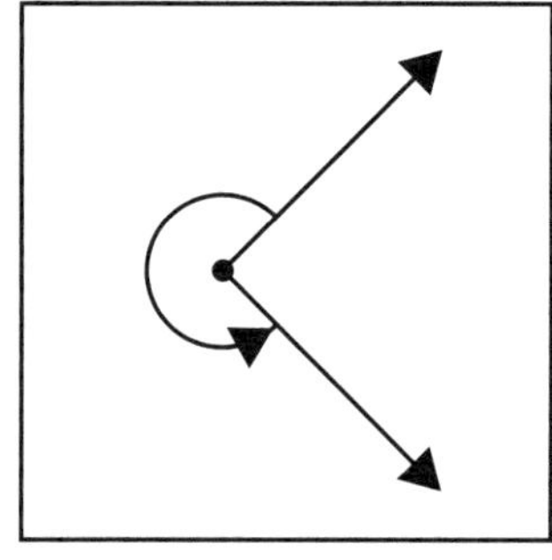

☐ right angles

7 The triangle is moved **1 square across** and **3 squares up**.
It is then turned clockwise through **2 right angles**.
Draw the new triangle in its **final** square.

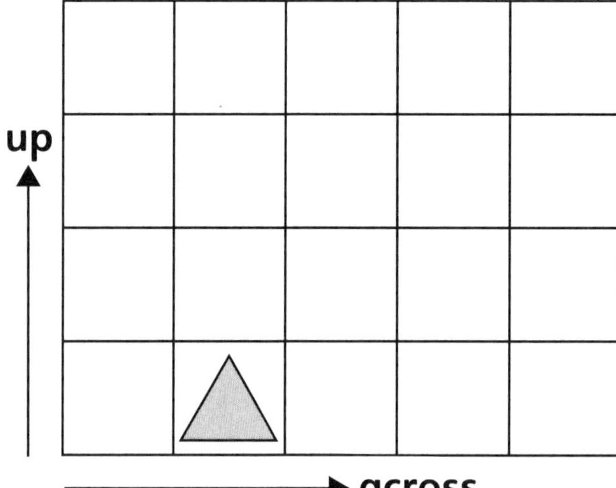

Year 2 Spring half-term • Written B

Test information and commentary chart

<table>
<tr><th>Q. no.</th><th>Objective</th><th>Block</th><th>Answer</th><th>Common difficulties and advice</th></tr>
<tr><td>1a, b</td><td>Count on and back in 1s or 10s from a 2-digit or 3-digit number; count on and back in 100s from a multiple of 100</td><td>A2</td><td>a) 20, 30, 29, 129
b) 300, 200, 201, 191</td><td>Many children do not recognise the correct direction of the arrows and work in the opposite direction to that of the question. Talk with children about arrows and arrowheads, together with the idea of inverse operations.</td></tr>
<tr><td>2</td><td>Begin to recognise odd and even numbers up to at least 50</td><td>A2</td><td><table><tr><th>number</th><th>is an even number</th><th>is an odd number</th><th>is both even and odd</th><th>is neither even nor odd</th></tr><tr><td>6</td><td>✓</td><td></td><td></td><td></td></tr><tr><td>77</td><td></td><td>✓</td><td></td><td></td></tr><tr><td>994</td><td>✓</td><td></td><td></td><td></td></tr><tr><td>51</td><td></td><td>✓</td><td></td><td></td></tr><tr><td>100</td><td>✓</td><td></td><td></td><td></td></tr></table></td><td>You may find some of the following errors:
77 is even as it has two digits the same;
77 is both even and odd as it ends in 7, but has two 7s;
994 is odd as the 9s are larger than the 4;
51 is even as it has two odd digits.</td></tr>
<tr><td>3</td><td>Count on and back in 1s or 10s from a 2-digit or 3-digit number</td><td>A2</td><td>Deidre 124, Vinnie 114, Imran 113, Jelena 123</td><td>Most children work out 114 correctly for Vinnie, but then write 115 (1 more than 114) for Imran. Give similar problems for children to do using objects and smaller numbers. Encourage them to check their answers.</td></tr>
<tr><td>4</td><td>Compare two or more 2-digit numbers</td><td>A2</td><td>For example:
19, 28, 37, 40</td><td>This question challenges children's understanding of place value. Many successfully use 1, 2, 3 and 4 as the missing digits; others choose a large digit for the first number and then find themselves running out of suitable digits. It is questions like this that encourage medium and high achievers to think more deeply about mathematical ideas.</td></tr>
<tr><td>5</td><td>Rehearse addition and subtraction facts for pairs of numbers that total up to 10</td><td>B2</td><td>2, 8, 19, 6, 15, 17, 9, 22, 8</td><td>The addition and subtraction of teen numbers causes most difficulties. Counting on or back large numbers is not easy as children lose track of where they get to in the count. Remind them of partitioning as an alternative approach.</td></tr>
<tr><td>6a, b</td><td>Know that a right angle is a measure of a quarter turn; recognise clockwise and anticlockwise turns</td><td>B2</td><td>a) 1
b) 3</td><td>3 right angles is a common error for part a. Do this practically with children walking with a hand pointing in the forward direction. The amount of turn is then easier to see. You can also use points of the compass if you feel children are ready for this. Similar difficulties may occur for part b.</td></tr>
<tr><td>7</td><td>Know that a right angle is a measure of a quarter turn; recognise clockwise and anticlockwise turns</td><td>B2</td><td>up
across</td><td>Many children are able to follow the translations correctly, but then fail to turn the triangle through two right angles. They need lots of practical activities turning a variety of shapes through different angles.</td></tr>
</table>

Year 2 Summer half-term • Written A

Name ....

1. Write the **missing** number names.

a) ______________ ↔ 32 b) ______________ ↔ 80

2. Write in the **missing** numbers.

a) 372 = ☐ **hundreds** ☐ **tens and** ☐ **units**

b) ☐ = 8 **hundreds** 0 **tens and** 5 **units**

3. **Round** each number to the **nearest 10**.

a) **41** —to the nearest 10→ ☐ b) **88** —to the nearest 10→ ☐

4. Work out the answers.

a) **37 + 4 =** ☐

b) **28 + 5 =** ☐

c) **19 + 3 =** ☐

5. Work out the difference in **length** between each pair of nails without measuring them.

a) ←17cm→ ←22cm→ ☐ cm b) ← 11cm → ←6cm→ ☐ cm

c) ← 8cm → ← 14cm → ☐ cm

6 a) Put a ring around **one-half** of the cows.

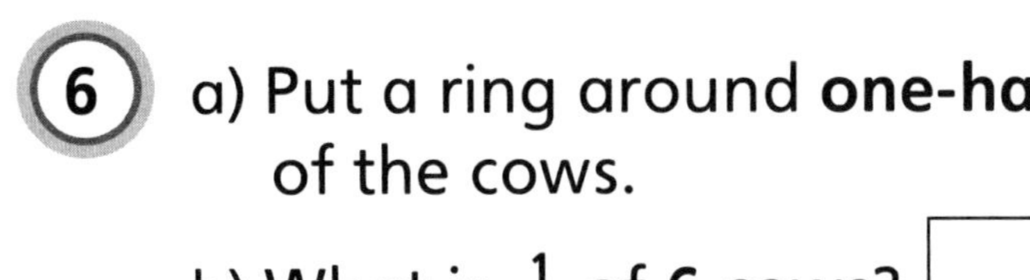

b) What is $\frac{1}{2}$ of **6** cows? ☐

7 a) Put a ring around **one-quarter** of the sheep.

b) What is $\frac{1}{4}$ of **12** sheep? ☐

8 Put a ring around $\frac{1}{2}$ or $\frac{1}{4}$ to show the fraction shaded.

a)

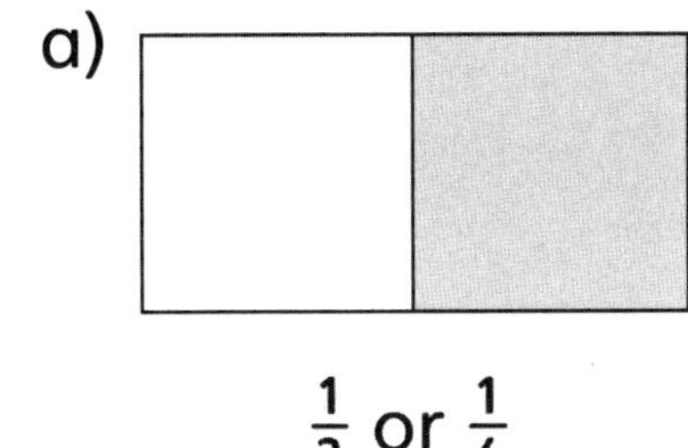

$\frac{1}{2}$ or $\frac{1}{4}$

b)

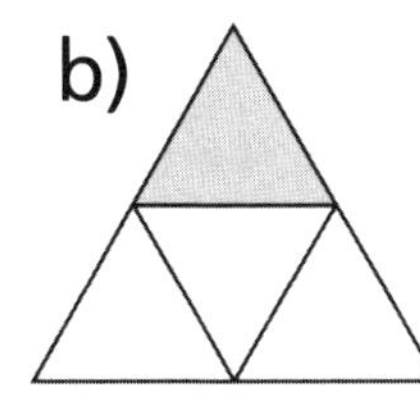

$\frac{1}{2}$ or $\frac{1}{4}$

c)

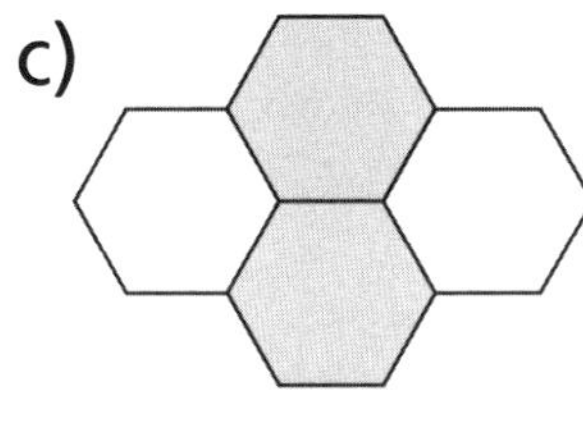

$\frac{1}{2}$ or $\frac{1}{4}$

9 Join pairs that make **100**.

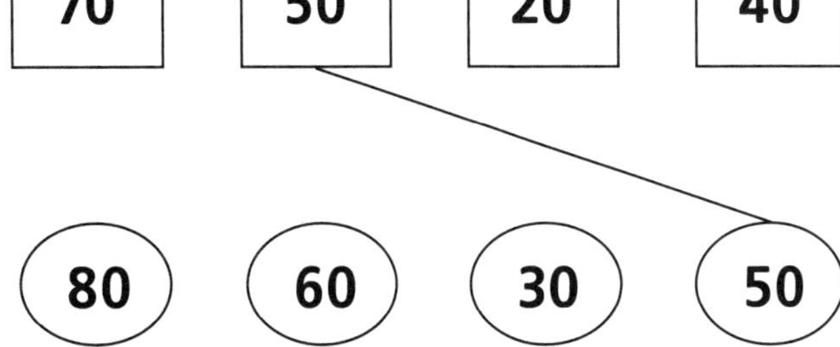

10 Here are **eight** number cards.

1	2	3	5	8	9	15	17

Use **all** eight cards once only to complete these additions.

a) ☐ + ☐ **= 10** b) ☐ + ☐ **= 10**

c) ☐ + ☐ **= 20** d) ☐ + ☐ **= 20**

11 Write in the **missing** numbers.

a) **57 +** ☐ **= 60** b) **25 +** ☐ **= 30**

12 Work out the answers.

a) Add **7** and **5**. ☐ b) Take **3** from **14**. ☐

Year 2 Summer half-term • Written A

Test information and commentary chart

Q. no.	Objective	Block	Answer	Common difficulties and advice
1a	Read and write numbers up to 100 in words	A3	thirty-two	Spelling is a problem here with 'thurty-two', 'therty-two' and 'tharty-two' frequently used. Although not a mathematical error, correct spelling of mathematical words is important and should not be ignored.
1b	Read and write numbers up to 100 in words	A3	eighty	A very small minority will write 8 as the answer. Look again at the match between names and numbers for the multiples of 10, using cards if necessary.
2a	Begin to partition 3-digit numbers into H, T and U	A3	3 hundreds, 7 tens, 2 units	A correct answer for this question does not mean children understand place value. Many use the order of the digits to write in the missing numbers. You may wish to ask questions with the place values in a different order, i.e. 486 = [ ] units [ ] hundreds [ ] tens
2b	Begin to partition 3-digit numbers into H, T and U	A3	805	The same comments apply here as to 2a.
3a	Begin to round numbers less than 100 to the nearest 10	A3	40	50 is a very common error. Use a number line to help children understand the idea of nearest 10. 40 41 50 A few children who have no concept of 'nearest 10' add 1 to 41 and write 42.
3b	Begin to round numbers less than 100 to the nearest 10	A3	90	80 is a very common error. Use a number line to help children understand the idea of nearest 10. 80 88 90 A few children who have no concept of 'nearest 10' add 1 to 88 and write 89.
4	Add a 1-digit number to a 2-digit number, crossing a multiple of 10	A3	a) 41 b) 33 c) 22	For children who have difficulty, provide a number line, and encourage them to count on by jumping along the line. An answer of 374 in part 4a would indicate a lack of appreciation of the place value aspect of these numbers.
5	Find the difference between two numbers, by counting on	A3	a) 5cm b) 5cm c) 6cm	For children who have difficulty, provide a number line and count how many jumps there are from the smaller number to the larger number.

Q. no.	Objective	Block	Answer	Common difficulties and advice
6a, b	Begin to recognise halves and quarters of small numbers of objects	B3	a) For example: b) 3	Some children do not recognise the relationship between the two parts of question 6 and may get one part correct and the other incorrect. When this occurs ask the children how they worked out each part of the question. It is important that children can 'picture' a fraction calculation when they do not how to perform the calculation.
7	Begin to recognise halves and quarters of small numbers of objects	B3	a) For example: b) 3	Some children do not recognise the relationship between the two parts of question 7 and may get one part correct and the other incorrect. When this occurs, ask the children how they worked out each part of the question. It is important that children can 'picture' a fraction calculation when they do not how to perform the calculation. The ringing of 4 sheep and writing $\frac{1}{4}$ of 12 as 4 is a common error. This is due to relating 'quarter' to the number 4.
8a, b, c	Begin to recognise halves and quarters of shapes	B3	a) $\frac{1}{2}$ b) $\frac{1}{4}$ c) $\frac{1}{2}$	Questions 8a and 8b are well answered. Incorrect answers for these suggest a total lack of understanding of unit fractions of shapes. $\frac{2}{4}$ is not an answer to be ringed in question 8c, as children are challenged to relate $\frac{2}{4}$ to $\frac{1}{2}$. As there are four hexagons in the shape, some children write $\frac{1}{4}$ as the answer, ignoring the number of hexagons shaded.
9	Know by heart pairs of multiples of 10 that total 100	B3	70 50 20 40 80 60 30 50	Search questions like this allow children to find pairs that they might otherwise not be able to calculate. Do not assume that children know every pair of multiples of 10 that make 100, even when they get this question totally correct.
10a, b	Know by heart addition and subtraction facts for pairs of numbers that total up to 10	B3	for example: a) 1 + 9 = 10 b) 2 + 8 = 10	Generally this is answered well. Incorrect answers include those with repeats of numbers. Children can be helped by giving them the same question, but with the eight numbers on cards and the four additions in frames. In this way a number cannot be repeated.
10c, d	Know by heart addition and subtraction facts for pairs of numbers that total 20	B3	c) 15 + 5 = 20 d) 17 + 3 = 20	As for 10a and b.

Q. no.	Objective	Block	Answer	Common difficulties and advice
11a	Use pairs that total 10 to make the next multiple of 10	B3	3	Some children write 4 as the answer. This is usually due to a counting on error with 57 included in the count. Use a number line to show that it is the 'jumps' that are counted not he numbers. 1 1 1 57 58 59 60
11b	Use pairs that total 10 to make the next multiple of 10	B3	5	6 is an error for similar reasoning as the 4 in question 11a.
12a	Know by heart addition and subtraction facts for pairs of numbers that total 20	B3	12	Those that reverse digits write '21' when the correct answer is '12'. Give such children practice in looking and talking about the differences of number cards that have digits reversed, such as 34 and 43.
12b	Know by heart addition and subtraction facts for pairs of numbers that total 20	B3	11	To some children the question 'Take 3 from 14' suggests 3 – 14, which they then cannot do. This results from the word from being seen as meaning 'subtract'.

Year 2 Summer half-term • Written B

Name ....

1. a) Write a 3-digit number that has **7 units**, **2 hundreds** and **6 tens** 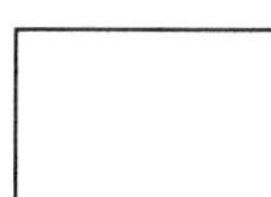

   b) A 3-digit number has **all** its digits **more than 5**. Write what the **3-digit** number could be 

2. Write in the **missing** numbers.

   a) **47 + 5 =** ☐

   b) **28 +** ☐ **= 32**

   c) ☐ **+ 6 = 84**

3. Complete the **subtractions**.

   a) **63 – 58 =** ☐

   b) **124 – 118 =** ☐

   c) **71 – 59 =** ☐

4. Write in the **missing** numbers.

   a) $\frac{1}{2}$ of **38 =** ☐

   b) $\frac{1}{2}$ of ☐ **= 15**

   c) $\frac{1}{4}$ of **52 =** ☐

   d) $\frac{1}{4}$ of ☐ **= 10**

5 The shaded shape is **one-half** of a rectangle.

Shade squares to **complete** the **whole** rectangle.

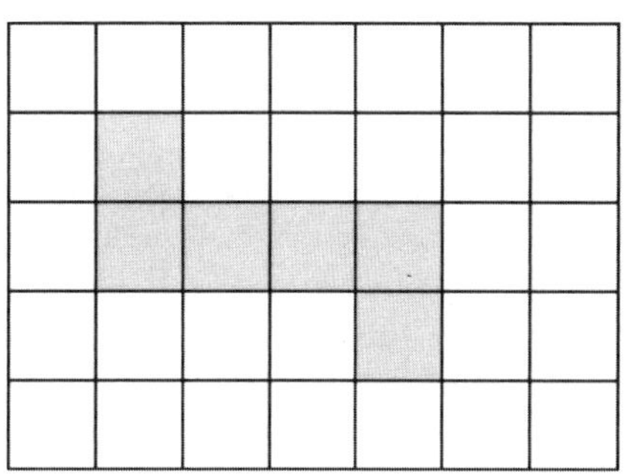

6 Complete the two **additions** in different ways.

	0	+			= 100			+		0	= 100

7 Write in what the **missing** digits **could** be.

					=		
a)	3		+	8	=		
b)		6	+		=	8	0

Year 2 Summer half-term • Written B

Test information and commentary chart

Q. no.	Objective	Block	Answer	Common difficulties and advice
1a	Begin to partition 3-digit numbers into H, T and U	A3	267	The order in which the value of the digits is given in the question causes difficulties for many children. It challenges those who have developed the strategy of using the order in which hundreds, tens and units are given to write the number. As you would expect a common error is 726. This does not mean that those who write 726 do not understand place value, but it does indicate that the strategy they have developed does not work on every occasion.
1b	Begin to partition 3-digit numbers into H, T and U	A3	For example: 687	This is an open question which some children find it difficult to respond to as these are many answers. Collect all the answers from the class and discuss why some are correct and others incorrect. You may wish to challenge your very high achievers to find how many possible solutions there are. (64 is the answer)
2	Add a 1-digit number to a 2-digit number, crossing a multiple of 10	A3	a) 52 b) 4 c) 78	Parts 2b and 2c are likely to cause more difficulty. As a strategy, children can use trial and improvement to lead them towards the correct solutions. Some may also find it helpful to use a number line to determine the starting point and the size of the jump required to reach the end point.
3	Find the difference between two numbers by counting on	A3	a) 5 b) 6 c) 12	The most difficult aspect is for children to appreciate that subtraction can be performed by counting on from the smaller to the larger. Part 3c is likely to be deemed the most difficult, involving a difference of more than 10. A number line can be used to illustrate finding the difference.
4a	Begin to recognise halves and quarters of small numbers of objects	B3	19	24 is a common error. Some children relate $\frac{1}{2}$ of 38 to the double of 24 as 38.
4b	Begin to recognise halves and quarters of small numbers of objects	B3	30	Many children do not understand the missing calculation and write $7\frac{1}{2}$ in the missing number box.
4c	Begin to recognise halves and quarters of small numbers of objects	B3	13	This is not well answered with a variety of errors and reasoning. The diagram below, which is based upon equal sharing, helps some with a trial and improvement approach when numbers are large. 52 ☐ + ☐ + ☐ + ☐ = 52

Q. no.	Objective	Block	Answer	Common difficulties and advice
4d	Begin to recognise halves and quarters of small numbers of objects	B3	40	This proves a difficult question for most children with $2\frac{1}{2}$ ($\frac{1}{4}$ of 10) common.
5	Begin to recognise halves and quarters of shapes	B3		A common error is children shading squares to make any rectangle, ignoring the information that what is shaded is one-half of the rectangle.
6	Know by heart pairs of multiples of 10 that total 100	B3	Any two from: 10 + 90 = 100 20 + 80 = 100… 80 + 20 = 100 90 + 10 = 100	A well answered question. You may wish to use this question as a class investigation by collecting together all the possible solutions and then ordering them. Interesting patterns emerge and discussion of the reasons for the patterns provides insight into additions of multiples of 10.
7a, b	Use pairs that total 10 to make the next multiple of 10	B3	a) For example: 32 + 8 = 40 b) For example: 76 + 4 = 80	A significant number of children write 2-digit numbers in boxes intended for single digits. Remind these children of the meaning of 'digit' as opposed to 'number'. For example: 3 0 + 10 = 4 0 7 0 + 10 = 8 0

About the End-of-term Written Tests

There are two end-of-term written tests for each term:

- **part A** is pitched at a level appropriate to all of the children in the class (except very low achievers)
- **part B** is written at an extension level; you may wish to give this selectively to higher achievers, possibly at a different time.

For each test there is an accompanying **Test Information and commentary chart** (containing *answers* to test questions, identifying the *objectives* being tested, and a *diagnostic commentary* for each question, highlighting common errors and how these may be addressed).

For each test there is also a **Class achievement record** sheet. This sheet lists all the objectives tested in a grid format so you can record individual children's achievement against the objectives according to their performance in the test. They can be found towards the end of this *Assessment Kit*, pages 149–156.

Both A and B tests assume that the 'default' ***Abacus Evolve*** sequence of blocks have been followed throughout the year to this point. The tests therefore contain questions relating to any of the Blocks A1–E1 (autumn), Blocks A2–E2 (spring), Blocks A3–E3 (summer).

If you have not taught some of these blocks, we suggest you check the **Test information and commentary chart** for each of Tests A and B to ensure that all questions relate to the teaching you have done.

Name ....

1 Write the **seasons** in **order**. Use these words.

summer | spring | winter

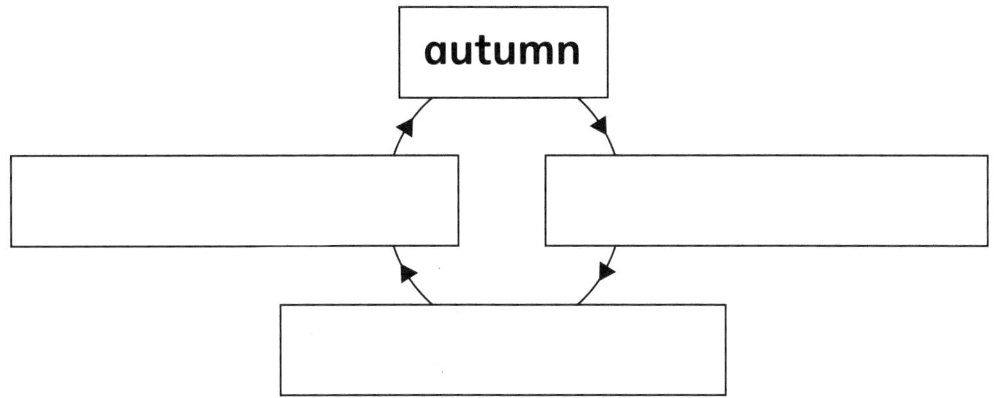

2 a) **Ring** each number that has **four tens**.

b) **Tick** (✓) each number that has **eight units**.

28 **84** **47** **54** **14** **40** **78**

3 Match each shape to its name.

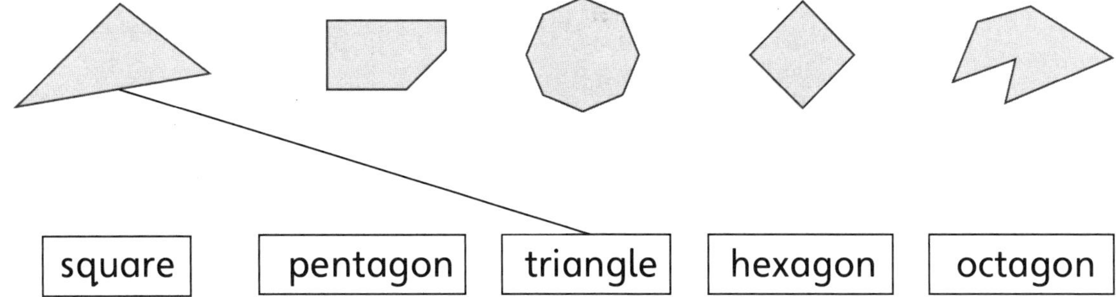

square | pentagon | triangle | hexagon | octagon

4 Write in the **missing** numbers.

a) **63** → ☐ **tens and** ☐ **units**

b) ☐ → **9** **tens and** **0** **units**

5 Complete the tables.

a)

number	4	8	2	1
number	3	2	7	6
sum	7			

b)

number	5	6	7	9
number	3	2	2	6
difference	2			

6 Draw the **line of symmetry** in each shape.

a) 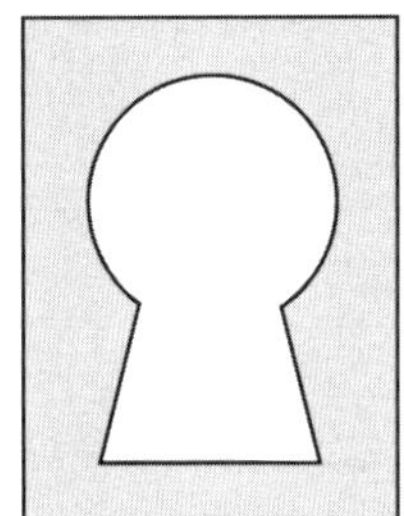

b) c) 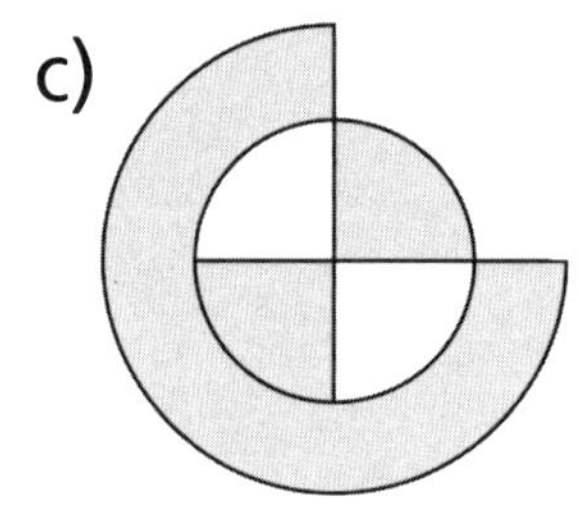

7 Write the numbers in order, **smallest** first.

34 48 83 38 84 43

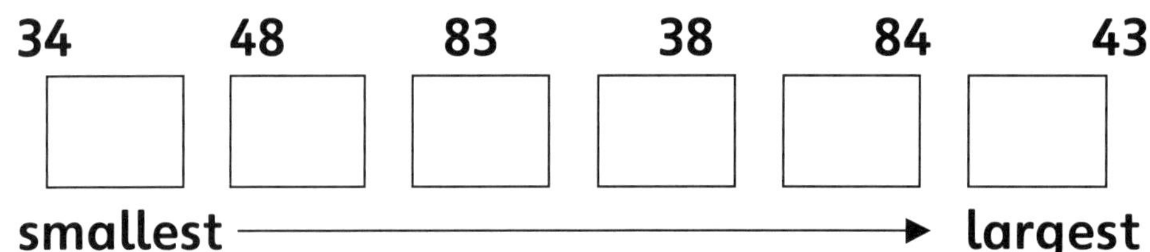

8 a) Write the number that the arrow is **pointing** to.

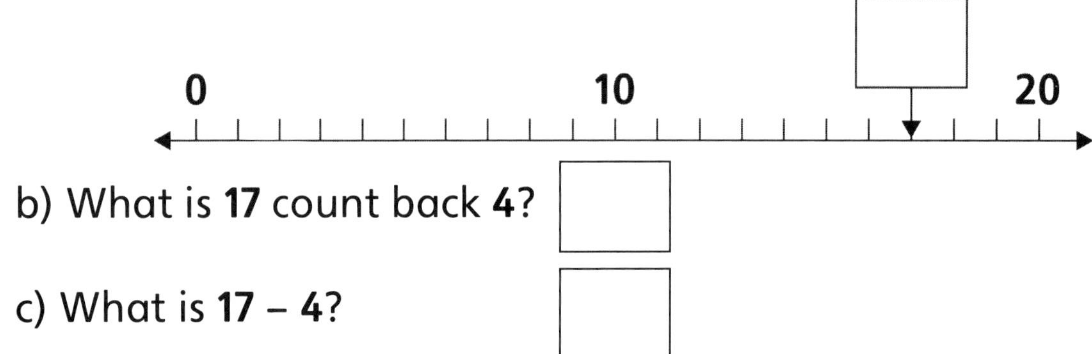

b) What is **17** count back **4**?

c) What is **17** – **4**?

9 Write in the **missing** numbers.

a) 3 —double→ ☐

b) 16 —halve→ ☐

10 Write in the **missing** numbers.

a) 7 —double→ ☐ —halve→ ☐

b) ☐ —halve→ 45 —double→ ☐

11 Work out the answers.

a) **26 + 8 =** ☐   b) **4 + 7 + 6 =** ☐

12 Claire went on holiday for **2 weeks**.
How many **days** was Claire on holiday? ☐ days

13 a) Draw more lines to make a rectangle.

b) Draw more lines to make a hexagon.

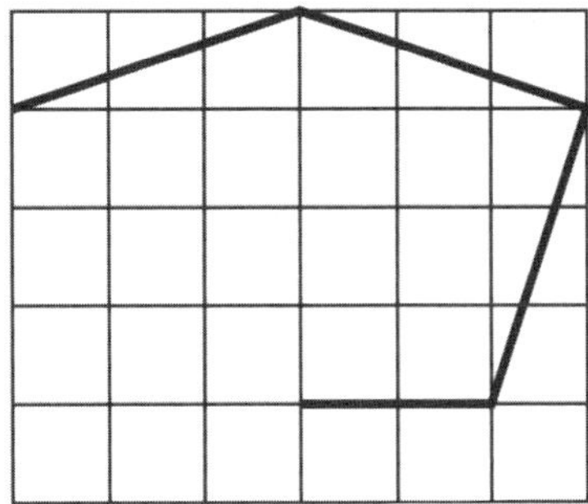

14 Here are **two** digit cards.

6   9

Write each digit in a box to complete this **subtraction**.
Find the **answer**.

☐ 3 – ☐ = ______

Year 2 Autumn end-of-term • Written A

Test information and commentary chart

Q. no.	Objective	Block	Answer	Common difficulties and advice
1	Use units of time and know the relationship between them: months in a year, seasons in a year	C1	autumn, summer, winter, spring	Children are accustomed to starting the cyclic order of the four seasons with spring. Having autumn already in a chart confuses some of them, who then write spring and summer in the next boxes after autumn and fill in the last box with winter. You can help children by having a large chart of the cyclic diagram, with the names of the seasons on card. These can be put on the activity table, perhaps with one season already positioned.
2a	Know what each digit in a 2-digit number represents, including 0 as a place holder	A1	Ringed numbers: 47, 40	A common error is to ring every number that has a '4' digit, irrespective of it being a ten or a unit. This confuses children when they then have to tick numbers for 2b. Suggest to such children that they should write T and U above the digits in each number before they ring or tick.
2b	Know what each digit in a 2-digit number represents, including 0 as a place holder	A1	Ticked numbers: 28, 78	As with 2a, a common error is to tick every number that has an '8' digit, irrespective of it being a ten or a unit. Suggest to such children that they should write T and U above the digits in each number before they ring or tick.
3	Use the names of common 2D shapes, including: pentagon, hexagon, octagon	D1	square, pentagon, triangle, hexagon, octagon	The convex irregular hexagon causes greatest difficulty. Too frequently, commercial charts that show polygons together with their names only illustrate regular ones. Check on your display in the classroom.
4a	Partition 2-digit numbers into T and U	A1	6 tens and 3 units	Question 4a is often very well answered, but its success can deceive you into believing children who get it correct understand place value. In fact, some children use the order of the digits and not their values to complete the empty boxes.
4b	Partition 2-digit numbers into T and U	A1	90	9 is a common error in 4b as children do not see the point in writing the 0, as 9 and 0 is 9.
5a	Rehearse addition and subtraction facts for pairs of numbers that total 10	B1	7, 10, 9, 7	Errors occur with 2 + 7 and 1 + 6. These are usually with children who do not recognise that the additions can be changed to 7 + 2 and 6 + 1. Because of this they count on from the smaller number and miscount, sometimes by using 2 in 2 + 7 as the first number, getting 8 as the answer. Show them using a number line that it is the 'jumps' that they should count not the numbers. 2 + 7: number line 2 3 4 5 6 7 8 9 with jumps of 1 7 + 2: number line 7 8 9 with jumps of 1
5b	Rehearse addition and subtraction facts for pairs of numbers that total 10	B1	2 4 5 3	The main error is children adding instead of finding the difference. Check that they understand what 'difference' means. Some children write 5 – 3 = 3. They do this by counting back three numbers: 5, 4, 3, and writing the last number they reached. Look out for those who give 5, 6 and 4 as their three answers.

Q. no.	Objective	Block	Answer	Common difficulties and advice
6a	Begin to recognise line symmetry	D1	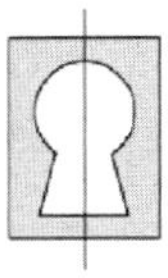	Children find shapes with a 'vertical' line of symmetry easy to recognise.
6b	Begin to recognise line symmetry	D1		Draw in vertical line of symmetry is a common error.
6c	Begin to recognise line symmetry	D1	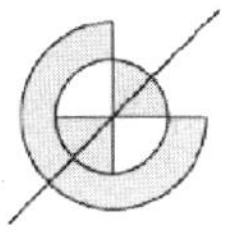	An oblique line of symmetry is the most difficult to recognise. Suggest to children that they turn the shape (here it would be the sheet of paper) until they see a line of symmetry. This would occur when it becomes 'vertical'.
7	Order numbers up to at least 100 and position them on a 100-square	A1	34, 38, 43, 48, 83, 84	The vast majority of children are able to put 2-digit numbers in order successfully. For the small minority, change the activity into one with number cards so that they can check what they have done and change positions if necessary. Discuss with them the strategy of comparing the tens digits first and then the units when the tens digits are the same.
8a	Extend understanding of subtraction as taking away	D1	17	Although the number line is marked in 1s, a common error is to see 10 as the previous number and write 11 in the box. Advise children to complete the labeling of marks with numbers before they work out the answer.
8b	Extend understanding of subtraction as taking away	D1	13	Some children do not see the relationships between the three parts to the question and give different answers for 8b and 8c, suggesting that they use different methods. Talk with children who do this as remedial activities are needed.
8c	Extend understanding of subtraction as taking away	D1	13	As 8b, above.
9a	Know by heart doubles for numbers up to at least 15 and corresponding halves	E1	6	This question should be answered well. Remind the few who have difficulty that double 3 = 3 + 3.
9b	Know by heart doubles for numbers up to at least 15 and corresponding halves	E1	8	Some children continue doubling when the question is about halving. Stress that they must always read questions carefully and not make assumptions about what they are to do.

Q. no.	Objective	Block	Answer	Common difficulties and advice
10a	Recognise halving as the inverse of doubling; Know by heart doubles for numbers up to at least 15 and corresponding halves	B1	7 → 14 → 7	A common mistake is to ignore that the second operation is 'halve' and to 'double' again. Talk with everyone about why the start and end numbers are equal.
10b	Recognise halving as the inverse of doubling; Know by heart doubles for numbers up to at least 15 and corresponding halves	B1	90 → 45 → 90	Similar errors occur here as in 10a.
11a	Add by counting on in 1s from the larger number, crossing a multiple of 10	E1	34	Some children who use partitioning rather than counting on write 214 as the answer. They have calculated 6 + 8 = 14 and not carried the ten. Look for those who count on and write 33 as the answer. This is due to counting 26 as one of the count on numbers. Use a number line to show the eight jumps.
11b	Add three numbers by putting the largest number first	E1	17	11 is a common error, with children adding 4 and 7, but then not completing the addition with the 6.
12	Use units of time and know the relationship between them: hours in a day, days in a week	C1	14 days	This question requires knowledge that there are seven days in one week. A variety of incorrect answers are to be found, mainly due to not having the necessary knowledge.
13a	Sort 2D shapes and describe their features: number of sides and corners	D1	For example: 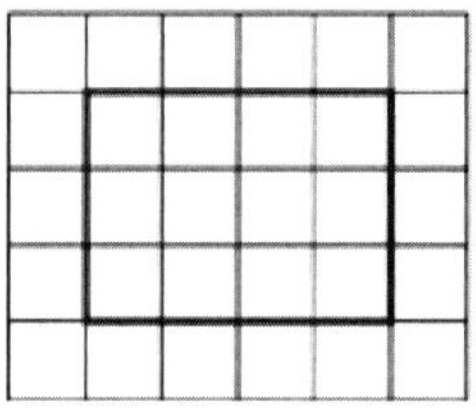	A few children ignore the instructions and draw one more line to complete a trapezium.
13b	Sort 2D shapes and describe their features: number of sides and corners	D1	For example: 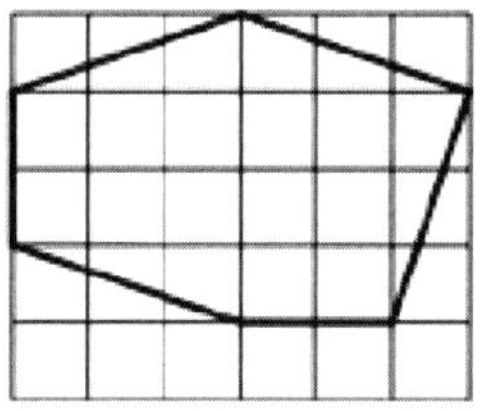	A few children ignore the instructions and draw one more line to complete a pentagon.

Q. no.	Objective	Block	Answer	Common difficulties and advice
14	Count back in 1s, crossing a multiple of ten, beginning to partition	D1	63 – 9 = 54 *or* 93 – 6 = 87	Counting back appears to be an appropriate method. However, some children write 63 – 9 = 66 or 93 – 6 = 93, indicating that they have use partitioning incorrectly by subtracting the units in the wrong order.

Name ....

1 Write in the **missing** numbers.

2 Here is a **count back in tens** sequence.
Write in the **missing** numbers.

3 These **four** numbers are in order.
Write in what the **missing** digits could be.

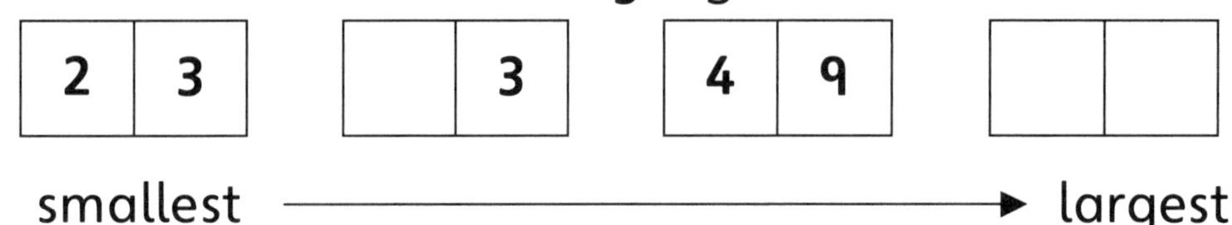

4 a) Draw more lines to make a shape that has 6 sides.

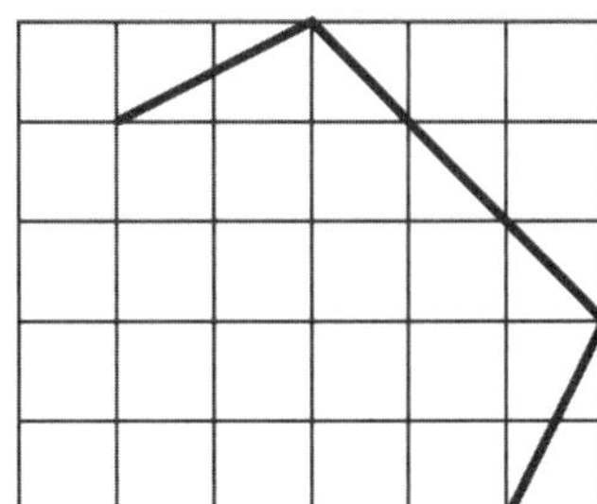

b) Draw more lines to make a shape that has 3 corners.

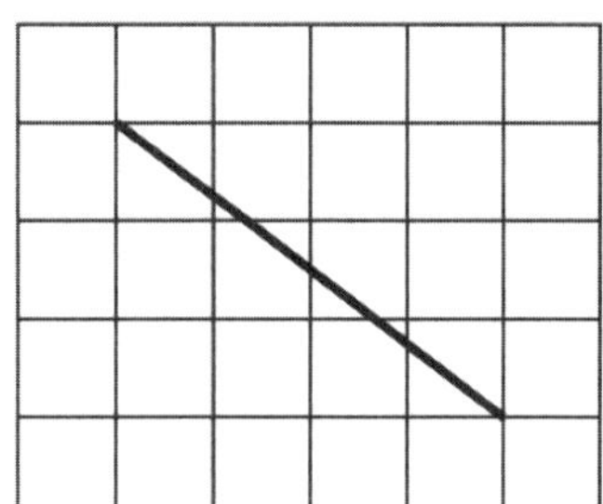

5 Alice says, ***'My number has two digits. The tens digit is double the units digit.'***
What could Alice's number be?

6 This **symmetrical** pattern has half missing.
Draw the **other half** of the pattern.

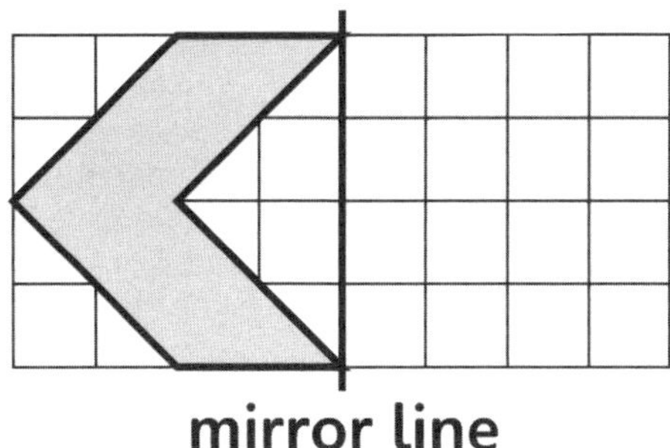

7 Complete the grids.

a) **addition**

+	5	7	
	11		
5			13
	7		

b) **subtraction**

–		3	
7			5
9	5		
		3	

8 Use these **three** number cards each time to complete four different subtractions.
The first has been started for you.

3 7 8

78 – 3 = ____ __ – _ = ____

__ – _ = ____ __ – _ = ____

Then find the answers.

Year 2 Autumn end-of-term • Written B

Test information and commentary chart

Q. no.	Objective	Block	Answer	Common difficulties and advice
1a	Partition 2-digit numbers into T and U	A1	1 unit and 7 tens	Many children do not look closely at the partition, assuming that the order of the place values is tens and then units. They write 7 units and 1 tens. Ask those who got it incorrect how they did it.
1b	Partition 2-digit numbers into T and U	A1	29	Many children make the same assumption as for 1a and write the number as 92. Draw their attention to the place values and ask what they now think the 2-digit number should be.
2	Count on and back in 1s or 10s from a 2-digit number	A1	77, 67, 57, 47, 37	A common error is to ignore the direction of the arrows and count back to the left, writing the first two numbers as 37 and 47. They then continue the sequence with the last two numbers being 67 and 77.
3	Order numbers up to at least 100 and position them on a 100-square	A1	For example: 23, 33, 49, 51	In general this question is answered well.
4a	Sort 2D shapes and describe their features: number of sides and corners	D1	For example:	Many children do not complete six sides, but draw only one more line to make a quadrilateral.
4b	Sort 2D shapes and describe their features: number of sides and corners	D1	For example:	Some children draw lines to make four or five corners. They fail to count the first corner, and some the last corner, as they count only those that they made with the lines they drew.
5	Know what each digit in a 2-digit number represents, including 0 as a place holder; Know by heart doubles for numbers up to at least 15 and corresponding halves	A1 E1	21 *or* 42 *or* 63 *or* 84	A common error is to make the units digit double the tens digit, writing 12, 24, 36 or 48.
6	Begin to sketch the reflection of a simple shape in a mirror line	D1	mirror line	A few children translate the shape to make this pattern: mirror line

<table>
<tr><th>Q. no.</th><th>Objective</th><th>Block</th><th>Answer</th><th>Common difficulties and advice</th></tr>
<tr><td>7a</td><td>Rehearse addition and subtraction facts for pairs of numbers that total 10</td><td>B1</td><td><table><tr><td>+</td><td>5</td><td>7</td><td>8</td></tr><tr><td>6</td><td>11</td><td>13</td><td>14</td></tr><tr><td>5</td><td>10</td><td>12</td><td>13</td></tr><tr><td>2</td><td>7</td><td>9</td><td>10</td></tr></table></td><td>Many children initially reason correctly and find the 6 as the first number on the left. Some do the same for other missing numbers. In general, however, many find that they are unable to sustain their reasoning and resort to guessing.</td></tr>
<tr><td>7b</td><td>Rehearse addition and subtraction facts for pairs of numbers that total 10</td><td>B1</td><td><table><tr><td>–</td><td>4</td><td>3</td><td>2</td></tr><tr><td>7</td><td>3</td><td>4</td><td>5</td></tr><tr><td>9</td><td>5</td><td>6</td><td>7</td></tr><tr><td>6</td><td>2</td><td>3</td><td>4</td></tr></table></td><td>Children approach this question in a similar way to 7a. Their guessing also involves addition.</td></tr>
<tr><td>8</td><td>Count back in 1s, crossing a multiple of ten, beginning to partition</td><td>D1</td><td>Any four from:
73 – 8 = 65
87 – 3 = 84
83 – 7 = 76
38 – 7 = 31
37 – 8 = 29</td><td>Despite the example, some children make ‘impossible’ subtractions, such as 38 – 87, by writing two digits in the 1-digit box for the second number. Others repeat digits not using one of the digits, for example 38 – 3.

Errors also occur when finding the answers. A typical error is 37 – 8 = 31, with the units digits being subtracted in the wrong order.</td></tr>
</table>

Year 2 Spring end-of-term • Written A

Name ....

1

a) How many cars are in **each** set? ☐

b) How many sets of **2** cars are there? ☐

c) How many cars are in **7** sets of **2** cars? ☐

2 Write in the **missing** numbers.

a) **1 more** than **79** is ☐

b) **1 less** than **90** is ☐

c) **10 more** than **58** is ☐

d) **10 less** than **28** is ☐

3

a) What is the value of **each** coin? ☐ p

b) How many **5p** coins are there? ☐

c) What is the **total** value of **6** lots of **5p**? ☐ p

4 What could the **missing** pairs of numbers be?
Make each pair **different**.

☐ + ☐ = 9   ☐ + ☐ = 9

☐ + ☐ = 9   ☐ + ☐ = 9

5 Write the answers.

a) **51 + 20 =** ☐   b) **68 − 50 =** ☐

6 Write the answers.

a) **44 + 21 =** ☐   b) **37 − 19 =** ☐

7 a) Draw a line to match each **3D shape** to its name.

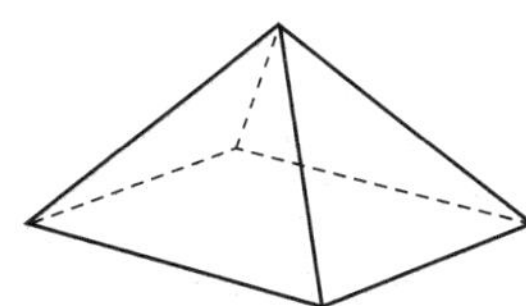
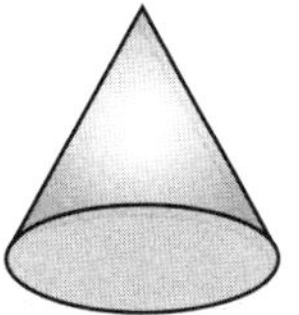
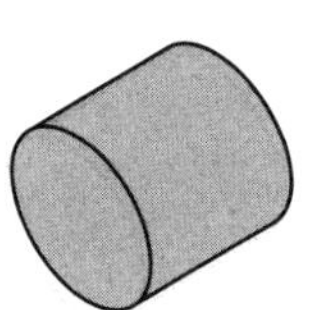

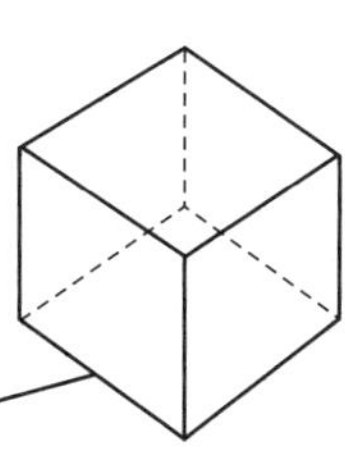

sphere	pyramid	cube	cone	cylinder

Write in the **missing** numbers.

b) A **cylinder** has ☐ flat surfaces and ☐ curved surface.

c) A **cube** has ☐ edges and ☐ corners.

d) A **square-based pyramid** has ☐ faces and ☐ edges.

8 Here is a pictogram of the **number of apples** children buy.

a) How many apples did **Clara** buy?

b) How many **more** apples did Alice buy than Harry?

c) **Altogether**, how many apples did the **three** children buy?

9 Start with 45.
Write in the **missing** numbers.

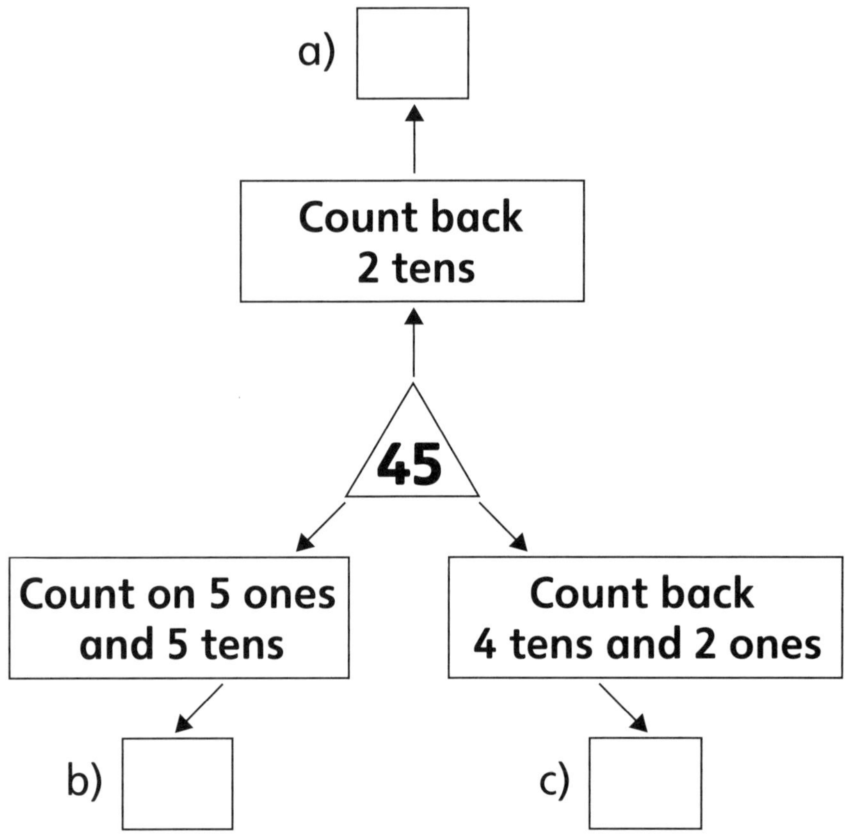

Year 2 Spring end-of-term • Written A

Test information and commentary chart

Q. no.	Objective	Block	Answer	Common difficulties and advice
1a	Introduce multiplication as 'lots of'	E2	2	This question is, and should be, answered correctly by the vast majority of children.
1b	Introduce multiplication as 'lots of'	E2	7	14 is a common error, with children counting all the cars anticipating that this is the next question. Encourage them to read every part of a question before starting to answer each part at a time. 4 also occurs with children reading the question as 'How many cars in 2 sets?'
1c	Introduce multiplication as 'lots of'	E2	14	This question becomes a counting exercise, which is achieved successfully by a large number. Talk with the children to find out who counted in 1s and who counted in 2s.
2a	Count on and back in 1s or 10s from a 2- or 3-digit number	A2	80	Very few get this incorrect.
2b	Count on and back in 1s or 10s from a 2- or 3-digit number	A2	89	For children who find 'less than' a difficult concept, change the question to 'more than' which they find easier. The two concepts '1 less than' and '1 more than' should be taught together. For example, '1 more than 89 is 90' is equivalent to '1 less than 90 is 89'. Show this using a number line.
2c	Count on and back in 1s or 10s from a 2- or 3-digit number	A2	68	66 is a common error caused by children increasing the 5 tens by 1 and then putting 6 for the units as 'they stay the same when finding 10 more or 10 less than'!
2d	Count on and back in 1s or 10s from a 2- or 3-digit number	A2	18	19 occurs frequently. This is due to children counting back, possibly using fingers, and including 28 as the first number in the count. Use a number line to show children that it is the 'jumps' that are counted, not the numbers.
3a, b, c	Introduce multiplication as 'lots of'	E2	a) 5p b) 6 c) 30p	For 3a, some write 30p the total value of the 6 coins, not of each coin. Encourage them to read every part of a question before they attempt to answer each part. 11 is a common error for 3c, as children add 6 and 5. This occurs when children have developed confidence in adding. They do not read a question, but look for the numbers and add.
4	Rehearse addition and subtraction facts for pairs of numbers that total up to 9	B1	Any four from: 0 + 9 1 + 8 2 + 7 3 + 6 4 + 5 5 + 4 6 + 3 7 + 2 8 + 1 9 + 0	This is answered extremely well. Look for those who use pattern to find the four pairs rather than do it randomly. Talk about how pattern helps find all ten pairs very quickly.
5a	Count on and back in 1s or 10s from a 2- or 3-digit number	D2	71	You may find that children who write numbers close to 71, i.e. 69 or 72, have counted on 20 and made an error in their counting. Invite children to talk about the strategies they used.
5b	Count on and back in 1s or 10s from a 2- or 3-digit number	D2	18	8 occurs as an incorrect answer. Here children 'see' the difference between 8 and 0 in the units and then forget to consider the tens. Remind them to check their answers by using the inverse operation.

Q. no.	Objective	Block	Answer	Common difficulties and advice
6a	Begin to add and subtract 19 and 21 by adding and subtracting 20	D2	65	Despite this question being answered correctly by most children, it is worth talking with them about the strategy they used. The two popular ones are add 20 and then an extra 1, and partitioning, finding 4 + 1 to give 5, then 4 + 2 to give 6 and then writing 65.
6b	Begin to add and subtract 19 and 21 by adding and subtracting 20	D2	18	22 is a common error with children finding the difference between 7 and 9 in the units. Some recognise that they cannot take 9 from 7 and change it to 9 take away 7.
7a	Use the names of common 3D shapes, including: cube, cuboid, cylinder, sphere, cone	D2	sphere pyramid cube cone cylinder	Some children find 2D representation of 3D shapes difficult. You may wish to ask the same question using actual 3D shapes. Also, children are helped by having a shape table on which there are name cards, actual shapes, pictures of shapes and 2D representations which they put into sets.
7b	Sort 3D shapes and describe their features: number of faces and corners	D2	2 and 1	Some children think that a cylinder has 2 curved surfaces, the front and the back. Let them move their hands around the curved surface to establish that there is only 1.
7c	Sort 3D shapes and describe their features: number of faces and corners	D2	12 and 8	4 and 4 are very common mistakes, being the number of sides and corners of a square. Handling a cube and placing small balls of Plasticene on edges and then corners means they can be counted more easily.
7d	Sort 3D shapes and describe their features: number of faces and corners	D2	5 and 8	3 faces is a common error. This occurs when children count the faces they can see and add 1 for the base. 4 edges is also common, which occurs when children think of the base, being a square, as having the only edges.
8a	Sort, organise and interpret information in a pictogram	C2	10	9 and 11 occur as answers when children miscount.
8b	Sort, organise and interpret information in a pictogram	C2	1	Some write 11 which is the total 5 and 6, not the difference.
8c	Sort, organise and interpret information in a pictogram	C2	21	Only a few do not realise that they have to count all the symbols. Talk with them that every apple is represented by a symbol.

Q. no.	Objective	Block	Answer	Common difficulties and advice
9	Count on in 2s, 5s or 10s up to 100	E2	a) 25 Count back 2 tens 45 Count on 5 ones and 5 tens Count back 4 tens and 2 ones b) 100 c) 3	Most children find counting back 2 tens easy. More make mistakes when counting on 5 ones and 5 tens. Some count on a 10, which is the sum of 5 (ones) and 5 (tens), getting 55 as the answer. A large number find counting back 4 tens and 2 ones difficult, not producing an answer. Talk about how a blank number line can help. 2 ones 4 tens 3 5 45

Year 2 Spring end-of-term • Written B

Name ....

1 Write in the missing numbers.

a) **3 sets of 5 =** ☐ b) ☐ **sets of 10 = 60**

c) **9 sets of** ☐ **= 18** d) ☐ **sets of** ☐ **= 30**

2 Here are six digit cards. **1** **2** **3** **4** **5** **6**

Use **all** six cards to make **one odd** and **two even** numbers **greater than 10**.

☐☐	☐☐	☐☐
odd	**even**	**even**

3 Write in the **missing** numbers.

a) 1 less than 40 = ☐ b) 10 less than 270 = ☐

c) 10 more than 491 = ☐ d) 10 less than 602 = ☐

4 Write in the **missing** numbers.

a) double 15 = half of ☐

b) half of 80 = double ☐

5 Here are **two** subtractions.
Complete **each** subtraction so that they are **different**.

☐ **7** – ☐ **0** = **3** ☐

☐ **7** – ☐ **0** = **3** ☐

6 Sam joins **two** identical **square-based pyramids** together.

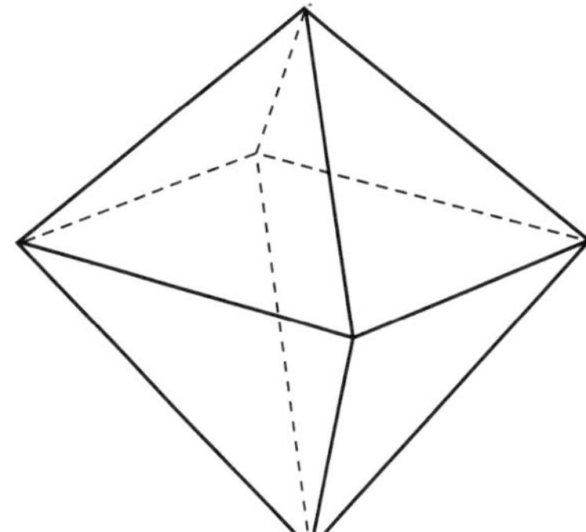

a) How many **faces** does the new shape have? ☐

b) How many **edges** does the new shape have? ☐

7 Write in the **missing** numbers.

a) 53 + 39 = ☐

b) 77 − 29 = ☐

Test information and commentary chart

Q. no.	Objective	Block	Answer	Common difficulties and advice
1a, b, c, d	Introduce multiplication as 'lots of'	E2	a) 15 b) 6 c) 2 d) Any two from: 2 sets of 15 3 sets of 10 6 sets of 5, etc.	In 1a, a few children add 3 and 5 to get 8, an incorrect answer. This shows that the question was read wrongly or a lack of understanding of 'sets of'. In both cases it is important that action is taken as the idea of 'lots of' and 'sets of' are fundamental to the understanding multiplication. You may find this incorrect method occurs also in the other three parts to question 1.
2	Begin to recognise odd and even numbers up to at least 100	E2	For example: 13, 64, 52	A typical error in this question is the repeated use of a digit, i.e. 35, 36, 12 as the three numbers. This type of open question can be used as a class investigation to find as many different ways as possible. It reinforces that it is the odd or even nature of the units digit which determines whether a number is odd or even, whatever the number of digits in the number. To avoid repeat use of digits, provide children with digit cards.
3a, b, c, d	Count on or back in 1s or 10s from a 2- or 3-digit number	A2	a) 39 b) 260 c) 501 d) 592	For 3a and 3b, more able children should find this easy. In 3c, some children may find difficulty with crossing 500. Possible common errors are 511, 591, 401. In 3d, some children may find difficulty with crossing 600, giving an error of 502.
4a	Begin to derive doubles of multiples of 5 up to 100 and the corresponding halves	E1	60	Only the most mathematically talented of children find the correct solution for this question, unless they have been taught a strategy. In this case the left-hand calculation should be worked out and the answer written above it. Children then see that the right-hand calculation should have this 'answer' and find it easier to work out the missing number. **30 = 30** **double 15 = half of** ☐
4b	Begin to derive doubles of multiples of 5 up to 100 and the corresponding halves	E1	20	The same advice applies to this problem as was outlined for 4a. **40 = 40** **half of 80 = double** ☐

Q. no.	Objective	Block	Answer	Common difficulties and advice
5	Subtract a multiple of 10 from a 2-digit number by counting back in 10s	D2	Any two from: 47 – 10 = 37 57 – 20 = 37 67 – 30 = 37 77 – 40 = 37 87 – 50 = 37 97 – 60 = 37	Here is an example of a trial and improvement strategy used to find one solution to this problem: 7 7 – 1 0 = 3 7 7 7 – 2 0 = 3 7 7 7 – 3 0 = 3 7 A class investigation could be conducted to find all six possible 'solutions' (note the use of this word as opposed to 'answers'). Ordering the solutions reveals the relationships inherent in the problem. Talking about these relationships helps children with strategies for solving similar problems.
6a, b	Sort 3D shapes and describe their features: number of faces and corners	D2	a) 8 b) 12	Although the hidden edges and faces are suggested, some children count two of the faces as one and get 7 as the answer. 7 and 8 are also popular errors for the number of edges. Make a 3D model of the shape using Polydron or similar shapes. Children can attach small balls of modelling clay to each face, then to each edge, and count them.
7a, b	Begin to add and subtract 19 and 21 by adding and subtracting 20	D2	a) 92 b) 48	7a assumes that children are comfortable with adding multiples of 10, and recognises the strategy of using this to add near multiples of 10. Otherwise, errors are likely to occur. In 7b, similar difficulties occur as in 7a, but in this case subtracting multiples of 10.

Year 2 Summer end-of-term • Written A

Name ....

1. Write the answers.

a) **15 + 16 =** ☐ b) **35 + 40 =** ☐

2. Write in the **missing** numbers.

a) **2 × 8 =** ☐ b) **5 × 7 =** ☐ c) **10 × 6 =** ☐

3. **Round** each number to the **nearest ten**.

a) **57** → ☐ b) **23** → ☐ c) **99** → ☐

4. Complete the table.

number	2	14	10	6	18
half of number	1				

5. Write the times shown on the clocks.

a) 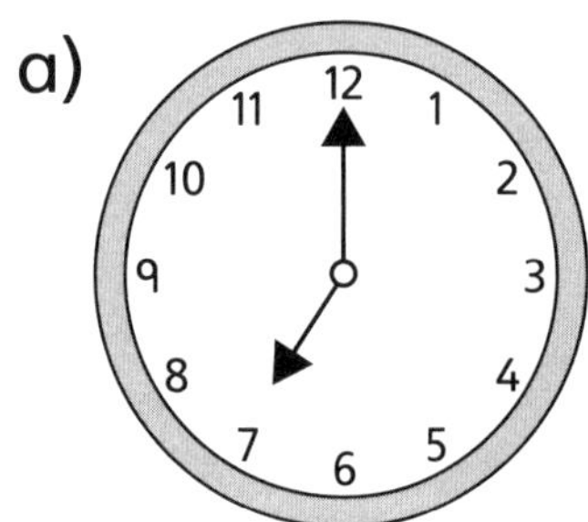

b) 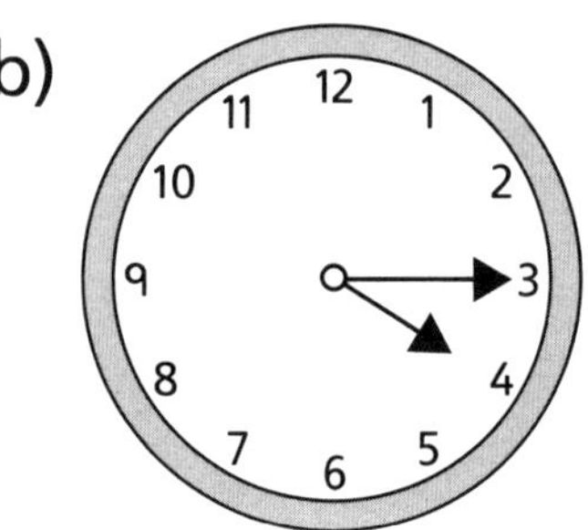

c) 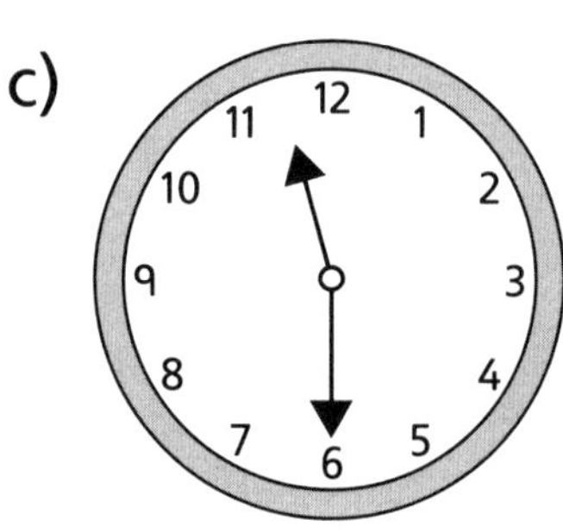

______________ ______________ ______________

6. Write in the **missing** numbers.

a) **8 +** ☐ **= 10** b) ☐ **+ 3 = 10**

c) **14 +** ☐ **= 20** d) ☐ **+ 11 = 20**

7 Write the answers.

a) **1** less than **60** is ☐

b) **1** more than **43** is ☐

c) **10** more than **53** is ☐

d) **10** less than **99** is ☐

e) Now write your four answers in **order**, largest first.

☐ ☐ ☐ ☐

largest → smallest

8 a) Write in the amount of the **jump** from **63** to **71**.

☐

63 **71**

b) What is **71 – 63**? ☐

9 In a box write how many **lines of symmetry** each letter has.

A **D** **M** **X** **Z**

☐ ☐ ☐ ☐ ☐

10 The table shows how many DVDs some children have.

Name	Number of DVDs
Dean	35
Bibi	22
Jodie	28
Adam	40

a) Who has the **fewest** DVDs? ____________

b) How many **more** DVDs does **Adam** have than **Jodie**? [ ]

c) How many **fewer** DVDs than **50** does **Dean** have? [ ]

11 Complete the subtractions and matching additions.

a) **23 –** [ ] **= 11** ←matches→ **11 +** [ ] **= 23**

b) **95 –** [ ] **= 58** ←matches→ **58 +** [ ] **= 95**

12 Write in the **missing** numbers.

a) [7] → (× 2) → [ ] → (÷ 2) → [ ]

b) [4] → (× 10) → [ ] → (÷ 10) → [ ]

c) [9] → (× 5) → [ ] → (÷ 5) → [ ]

d) [5] → (× 4) → [ ] → (÷ 4) → [ ]

13 Write the answers.

a) **34 + 25 =** [ ]

b) **46 + 18 =** [ ]

14 The cat catches the mouse.

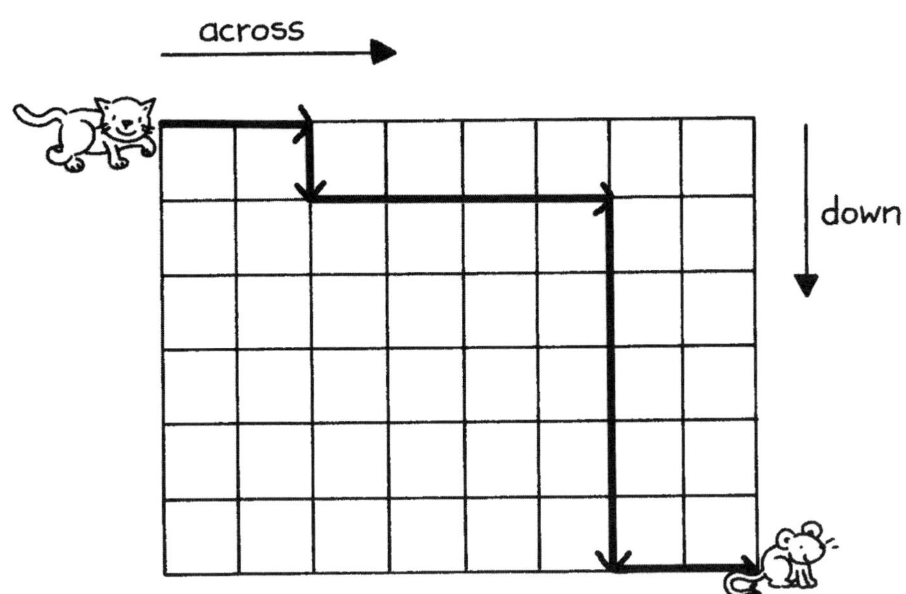

Complete the **instructions** for the path.

across 2 **down 1** ______ ______ ______

15 Write the answers.

a) **44 + 50 =** ☐ b) **62 + 20 =** ☐

16 Write the answers.

a) **57 + 19 =** ☐ b) **73 − 19 =** ☐

17 Frances has these coins in her purse.

a) How much has she in her purse? £ ☐

b) How much **more** does she need to make **£5**? £ ☐

18 a) Simon thinks of a number. He says,
"When I add 7 to my number, the answer is 607."

What is Simon's number? ☐

b) Theresa thinks of a number. She says,
"When I subtract 4 from my number, the answer is 196."

What is Theresa's number? ☐

19 Harry said the 2, 5 and 10 times tables in $\mathbf{1\frac{1}{2}}$ minutes.
Becky said them in **100 seconds**.

a) Who said the tables in the **shortest** time? ______________

b) By how many **seconds** shorter was it? ☐ seconds

Year 2 Summer end-of-term • Written A

Test information and commentary chart

Q. no.	Objective	Block	Answer	Common difficulties and advice
1a, b	Add by identifying near doubles for multiples of 5	E3	a) 31 b) 75	For part a), children who not see these as near doubles add 5 and 6 to get 11 and 1 and 1 to get 2, and write 211. In b), some add the 4 to 35 and get 39, ignoring the zero as zero is treated as nothing.
2a, b, c	Know by heart the multiplication facts for 2, 5 and 10 times-tables	E3	a) 16 b) 35 c) 60	Questions 2a (2 × 8) and 2c (10 × 6) are easier than 2b (5 × 7). At this time of Year 2, the three questions should elicit responses from memory. Answers such as 25, 36 and 37 show that this particular fact, 5 × 7, causes some children difficulties. Show those who make errors how to use the pattern in the 5 times table to check on the accuracy of their knowledge.
3a, b, c	Begin to round numbers less than 100 to the nearest 10	A3	a) 60 b) 20 c) 100	Although rounding to the nearest ten is answered well, do not assume that it is the low achievers who make errors. The three answers 67, 33 and 199 made by an 'average' child show total misunderstanding of the concept. Use a number line to establish 'nearest ten'.
4	Know by heart doubles for numbers up to at least 15 and the corresponding halves	E1	1, **7**, **5**, **3**, **9**	Only half of 18 causes difficulties. Remind children that they should double to check their answer and, if it is not correct, possibly to use trial and improvement to find the correct answer.
5a, b, c	Read the time to the quarter hour on analogue and 12-hour digital clocks	D3	a) 7 o'clock d) quarter past 4 e) half past 11	Only a very few children at the end of Year 2 will not be telling the time correctly to half and quarter hours. Where errors occur it is often due to mixing up the two hands. For example, half past 11 is written as 6 o'clock.
6a	Know by heart addition and subtraction facts for pairs of numbers that total up to 10	B3	2	This question should be answered correctly by the vast majority of children. Ask those who do not answer correctly how they worked out the answer and provide appropriate help.
6b	Know by heart addition and subtraction facts for pairs of numbers that total up to 10	B3	7	8 is a common error. As with similar questions in previous tests, children who count on from 3 to 10 sometimes include 3 in their count. Children who count back from 10 to 3 may include 10 in their count. Remedial activities will be necessary to unlearn a learnt procedure. Lots of work with the number line together with practical work with objects will help.
6c	Know by heart addition and subtraction facts for pairs of numbers that total 20	B3	6	7 is a common error for the same reasons as explained in 6b.
6d	Know by heart addition and subtraction facts for pairs of numbers that total 20	B3	9	10 is a common error for the same reasons as explained in 6b.

Q. no.	Objective	Block	Answer	Common difficulties and advice
7a, b, c, d	Count on and back in 1s or 10s from a 2- or 3-digit number	A2	a) 59 b) 44 c) 63 d) 89	'1 more than' and '10 more than' should not prove difficult. Although the same can be said of the 'less than' questions, it is well known that they are more difficult than 'more than' questions. Errors are sometimes made in counting back, but usually it is because children do not understand the concept and hence are unable to work with it successfully. Suggest to children using number tracks, lines or grids how they can count back to find the answers. Make a list of '1 less than' questions and talk about what happens to the digits of numbers when '1 less than' is found. Do the same for '10 less than'. Also relate '1 more than' and '1 less than'. For example, '1 more than 60 is 61' leads to the relation '1 less than 61 is 60', the two being equivalent.
7e	Order numbers up to at least 100 and position them on a 100-square	A1	89, 63, 59, 44	This question should be marked on the basis of the answers, whether correct or incorrect, in 7a, 7b, 7c and 7d.
8a, b	Find the difference between two numbers by counting on	A3	a) 8 b) 8	7 is a common error for question 8a as children count not the magnitude or value of the jump, but how many numbers has it jumped over, that is 64, 65, 66, 67, 68, 69, 70 – a total of seven numbers. 67 is also a error that some children make as they read the diagram to mean find the number on the number line that is below, or halfway between, the empty box which is 67. A few children write 7 for 8a and 8 for 8b, not recognising the relationship between the two questions and obviously using different methods to solve them.
9	Begin to recognise line symmetry	D1	A has 1 D has 1 M has 1 X has 2 Z has 0	Many children write that Z has one line of symmetry. Provide them with a mirror to check.
10a, b, c	Interpret information from a table	C3	a) Bibi b) 12 c) 15	Question 10a is found to be easy by most children. Question 10b demands finding the difference between 40 and 28. 13 is a common error as children count on or back incorrectly. It is the word 'fewer' that causes difficulty in 10c, with a variety of answers which show few common errors except the usual 16, a count on or back error.
11a	Understand that subtraction is the inverse of addition, using missing number sentences	D3	23 – 12 = 11 11 + 12 = 23	Some children get the subtraction correct and then do not use the three numbers to write correctly the matching addition. For example, 12 is written for the subtraction and 13 for the addition. This indicates that the child used different methods to find the missing numbers.

Q. no.	Objective	Block	Answer	Common difficulties and advice
11b	Understand that subtraction is the inverse of addition, using missing number sentences	D3	95 – 37 = 58 58 + 37 = 95	More errors occur with 11b than 11a as the numbers are larger, and crossing tens is necessary for the subtraction. A common error is 43 for the subtraction, which children get by taking 5 from 8 rather than 8 from 5 in the units, and 5 from 9 in the tens. They then proceed to write 43 in the addition without checking its accuracy. Also the correct 37 is written in the subtraction and 38 in the addition, not understanding the equivalence between the two calculations.
12a, b, c, d	Begin to understand division as the inverse of multiplication	E3	a) 7 → 14 → 7 b) 4 → 40 → 4 c) 9 → 45 → 9 d) 5 → 20 → 5	You are likely to find that more errors occur with question 12a and 12c than with 12b and 12d. Most children get the last two questions correct, which could suggest that these children understand the inverse relationship between multiplication and division. However, answers such as 7, 14, 6 and 7, 14, 28 for 12a and 9, 45, 6 and 9, 45, 8 for 12c suggest otherwise. Interestingly, an answer such as 7, 18, 7, although containing incorrect calculations, suggests that the child has some understanding of the inverse relationship.
13a	Add two 2-digit numbers using an appropriate strategy	D3	59	Most children get the correct answer with many calculating 4 + 5 and 3 + 2. Some do this as a procedure that lacks understanding of the place value concepts involved. Look for those who write the addition in standard vertical format. This suggests their lack of confidence in mental methods.
13b	Add two 2-digit numbers using an appropriate strategy	D3	64	Those who got the correct answer for 13a but did not understand the place value concepts they were using, get 514 as the answer. This results from the procedure 6 + 8 = 14, write down the 14; 4 + 1 = 5, write down the 5. This is exactly what they did in 13a with success.
14	Give instructions for moving along a route in straight lines and round corners	B2	across 4 down 5 across 2	Some write 'across, down, across' without specifying the amounts. Talk with them about the method of finding a correct answer.
15a	Count on and back in 1s or 10s from a 2- or 3-digit number	D2	94	You are likely to find that some children write 44 + 50 in a vertical format and not work it out mentally. This should not be surprising as children have to recognise the type of addition it is and then choose the appropriate mental strategy. This results in errors such as 90 and 84. Show them how the number line helps them to count on in 10s.
15b	Count on and back in 1s or 10s from a 2- or 3-digit number	D2	82	62 is a common error. This results from children recognising that 20, a multiple of 10, has to be added and that this does not change the unit digit. They then forget to add 2 tens to the 6 tens.
16a	Begin to add and subtract 19 and 21 by adding and subtracting 20	D2	76	Here, as with questions 15a and 15b, children have to recognise the type of addition and then choose the appropriate mental strategy of adding 20 and subtracting 1. Some find it easier to write 57 + 19 vertically, whatever the type of addition. Whichever method is chosen, a common error is 616, with children following a procedure that does not work when 'carrying' is involved.

Q. no.	Objective	Block	Answer	Common difficulties and advice
16b	Begin to add and subtract 19 and 21 by adding and subtracting 20	D2	54	Adding instead of subtracting is common with the answer as 92.
17a	Find totals of sets of coins: relate to adding three or more numbers	E1	£1·88	It is important that children have a strategy when counting coins. Those who do, do not make errors by counting coins more than once or omitting coins from the count. Discuss strategies that have been used and suggest one that children find they can use successfully.
17b	Find totals of sets of coins: relate to adding three or more numbers	E1	£3·12 *or* the difference between the answer to 17a and £5	Working with static pictures of coins is very difficult for some children. Use real coins with those who get this incorrect to check if they can then do the question correctly.
18a	Add and begin to subtract a 1-digit number to and from multiples of 10 and 100	C3	600	614 is a common error as children add 7 to 607. A number line can help children visualise what is involved in the question using ? as the number Simon thinks of. +7 ? 607
18b	Add and begin to subtract a 1-digit number to and from multiples of 10 and 100	C3	200	192 is a common error as children subtract 4 from 196. As in 18a, a number line will help. -4 196 ?
19a, b	Use units of time and know the relationship between them: hours, minutes, seconds	D3	a) Harry b) 10 seconds	This question requires both the knowledge that there are 60 seconds in 1 minute, the calculation to find $\frac{1}{2}$ of 60 and then the addition of 60 and 30 to find $1\frac{1}{2}$ minutes in seconds. Check that those who write Harry as the answer to 19a were not guessing. 90 seconds is a common error for 19b as children write the number of seconds it takes Harry, rather 10 seconds, which is the difference between the two times.

Year 2 Summer end-of-term • Written B

Name ....

1. Write in the **missing** numbers.

   a) **5** × ☐ = **45** b) **2** × ☐ = **12** c) **10** × ☐ = **80**

2. Here are **six** number cards.

2	4	5	7	9	13

   Use **all** six cards once only to complete these two additions.

   a) ☐ + ☐ + ☐ = 20 b) ☐ + ☐ + ☐ = 20

3. Here are **two** additions.
   Complete each addition so that they are **different**.

   ☐ 8 + 7 = ☐ ☐ ☐ 8 + 7 = ☐ ☐

4. Find the **differences** between:

   a) **54** and **26** ☐ b) **154** and **26** ☐

   c) **32** and **91** ☐ d) **32** and **191** ☐

5. Complete the tables.

   a)

number	**4**		**30**
double		**18**	

   b)

number		**20**	
halve	**6**		**50**

6 Write in the **missing** numbers.

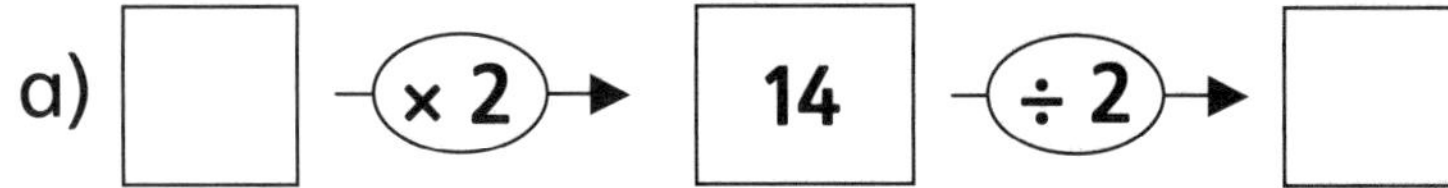

a) ☐ —(× 2)→ 14 —(÷ 2)→ ☐

b) ☐ —(× 5)→ ☐ —(÷ 5)→ 6

c) ☐ —(× 10)→ 90 —(÷ 10)→ ☐

d) ☐ —(× 4)→ ☐ —(÷ 4)→ 8

7 Find the missing digits for the **subtractions** and the **matching additions**.

a) ☐3 − 4☐ = 37 ←matches→ 37 + 4☐ = ☐3

b) 8☐ − ☐8 = 26 ←matches→ 26 + ☐8 = 8☐

8 Write a **different pair** of **numbers** to complete each sentence.

a) $\frac{1}{2}$ of ☐ = $\frac{1}{4}$ of ☐ b) $\frac{1}{2}$ of ☐ = $\frac{1}{4}$ of ☐

9 Here are six digit cards. 9 8 7 6 5 4

Use **all** six cards to make **one odd** and **two even** numbers to complete this number sentence.

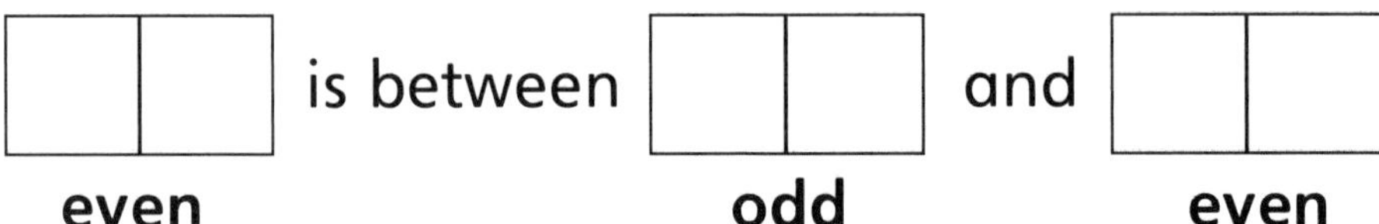

☐☐ is between ☐☐ and ☐☐

even **odd** **even**

10 a) Find the **answer** to the **subtraction**.
Complete a matching **addition**.

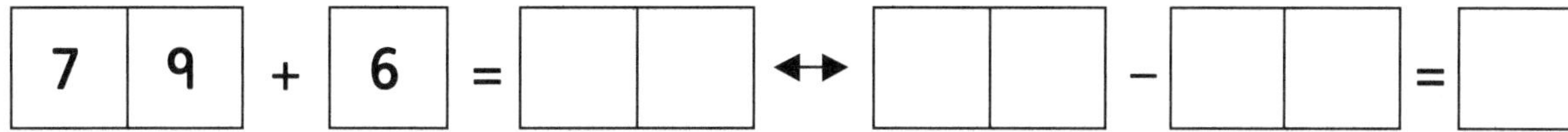

5	3	−	4	6	=		↔			+		=		

b) Find the **answer** to the **addition**.
Complete a matching **subtraction**.

7	9	+	6	=			↔			−			=	

Year 2 Summer end-of-term • Written B

Test information and commentary chart

<table>
<tr><th>Q. no.</th><th>Objective</th><th>Block</th><th>Answer</th><th>Common difficulties and advice</th></tr>
<tr><td>1a, b, c</td><td>Know by heart the multiplication facts for 2, 5 and 10 times-tables</td><td>E3</td><td>a) 9
b) 6
c) 8</td><td>The three questions should prove to have little difficulty for the high achievers. Errors that do occur are the result of children multiplying the two numbers rather than using division, the inverse operation.</td></tr>
<tr><td>2a, b</td><td>Begin to add three 1-digit numbers mentally;
Know by heart addition and subtraction facts for pairs of numbers that total 20</td><td>B2, B3</td><td>a) 2 + 5 + 13 = 20
b) b) 4 + 7 + 9 = 20</td><td>Some children, cleverly, write the same three numbers twice but in a different order, i.e. 5 + 2 + 13 = 20 and 13 + 2 + 5 = 20. This does not satisfy the condition that 'all six cards' are to be used. Advise children that when they are answering questions that involve the use of number or digit cards, to tick or cross a card when they have used it.</td></tr>
<tr><td>3a, b</td><td>Add a 1 digit number to a 2 digit number, crossing a multiple of 10 (rehearse)</td><td>A3</td><td>Any two from:
18 + 7 = 25
28 + 7 = 35 …
78 + 7 = 85
88 + 7 = 95</td><td>A frequently occuring error is the use of a zero as a tens digit. You may also find children who complete one open addition correctly, say 18 + 7 = 25, then produce an incorrect one, say 68 + 7 = 72. You should discuss this anomaly with such children as the reason can vary from child to child. This question also lends itself to an investigation, which can end with the eight possible additions being ordered and patterns discussed.</td></tr>
<tr><td>4a, b, c, d</td><td>Subtract one 2-digit number from another using an appropriate strategy</td><td>D3</td><td>a) 28
b) 128
c) 59
d) 159</td><td>A common error in 4a is 32, which arises when children calculate 4 from 6 instead of 6 from 4 in the units. This is repeated in 4b as 132, 4c as 61 and 4d as 161.

Some children who get 4a correct fail to see the relationship between 4a and 4b and write an incorrect answer for 4b. This also occurs with 4c and 4d.

You will also find some children finding the sum of each pair of numbers. This may occur as they respond to the word 'and' between the numbers as suggesting addition.</td></tr>
<tr><td>5a, b</td><td>Know by heart doubles for numbers up to at least 15 and corresponding halves;
Double multiples of 5 up to 50;
Halve multiples of 10 up to 100</td><td>E1</td><td>a)<table><tr><td>number</td><td>4</td><td>9</td><td>30</td></tr><tr><td>double</td><td>8</td><td>18</td><td>60</td></tr></table>b)<table><tr><td>number</td><td>12</td><td>20</td><td>100</td></tr><tr><td>halve</td><td>6</td><td>10</td><td>50</td></tr></table></td><td>High achievers should be able to double and halve simple numbers correctly. If errors do occur with finding which number doubled gives 18 and which number halved gives 50, show children that they can think of double and halve as operations using a number line. For example:
[ ] double → 18
[ ] halve → 50
and use the inverse operation.</td></tr>
<tr><td>6a, b, c, d</td><td>Begin to understand division as the inverse of multiplication</td><td>E3</td><td>a) 7 → 14 → 7
b) 6 → 30 → 6
c) 9 → 90 → 9
d) 8 → 32 → 8</td><td>Generally mistakes are more likely when children do not understand that multiplication and division are inverse operations. However, there are some children who do not recognise the direction of the arrows and work in the incorrect direction. For example:
28 (×2) → 14 (÷2) → 7   [ ] (×5) → 1r1 (÷5) → 6
900 (×10) → 90 (÷10) → 9   8 (×4) → 2 (÷4) → 8</td></tr>
</table>

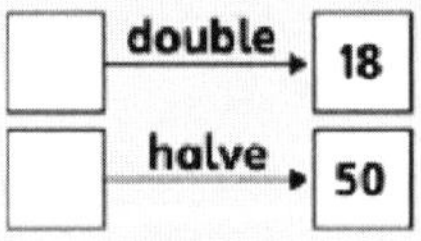

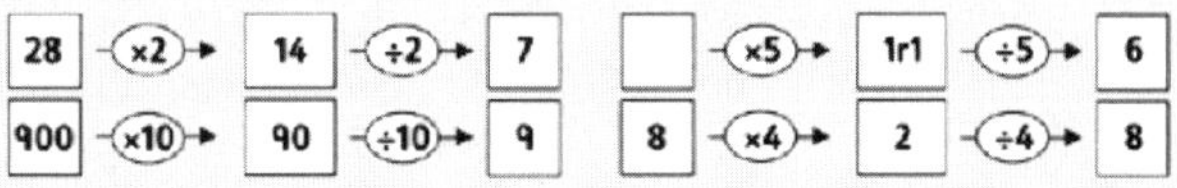

Q. no.	Objective	Block	Answer	Common difficulties and advice
7a, b	Understand that subtraction is the inverse of addition, using missing number sentences	D3	a) 83 – 46 = 37 37 + 46 = 83 b) 84 – 58 = 26 26 + 58 = 84	In 7a a common error for the subtraction is 73 – 44 = 37, with children subtracting the 3 from the 7 in the two given units and then adding 3 to 7 to get 7 for the tens. This error would be recognised if, when the digits were written in the matching addition as 37 + 44 = 73, it had been checked. This is one of the reasons for placing such emphasis on inverse operations and matching calculations. Many children make a similar error in 7b writing 82 – 68 = 26 matches 26 + 68 = 82.
8a, b	Recognise fraction notation; Begin to recognise halves and quarters of shapes	B3	For example: a) $\frac{1}{2}$ of 10 = $\frac{1}{4}$ of 20 b) $\frac{1}{2}$ of 18 = $\frac{1}{4}$ of 36	Errors in 8a and 8b are often due to children interpreting the '=' sign to mean 'find the answer'. This results in children writing: $\frac{1}{2}$ of [8] = 4 $\frac{1}{4}$ of [20] = 5 They treat each side of the = sign as a calculation unrelated to the other. Whenever possible, use 'has the same value as' for the = sign.
9	Begin to recognise odd and even numbers up to at least 100; Say a number lying between two numbers, up to at least 100	A2	For example: 64 is between 57 and 98	Some errors are caused by children using a digit card more than once. Encourage them to tick or cross a card when they have used the digit.
10a	Find the difference between two numbers by counting on	B2	7 and 46 + 7 = 53	The idea of a subtraction and an addition being equivalent (here 'match' is used) is not an easy idea for young children This is what one high achiever wrote. [5][3] – [4][6] = [1] ↔ [4][6] + [4] = [4][7] The same child knew the answer to 53 – 46 when presented separately and was confused by the matching presentation. Provide children two sets of three numbers that make an addition and a subtraction. Working with cards allows children to use trial and improvement with earlier attempts not apparent.
10b	Begin to add by bridging a multiple of 10 (36 + 8 = 36 + 4 + 4)	B2	85 and 85 – 79 = 6	Similar difficulties occur for some children when given the addition first. Here is what another high achiever did. [7][9] + [6] = [8][4] ↔ [7][8] – [3][4] = [6] The advice given for 7a applies here also.

Mark Scheme and End-of-term Levelled Guidance

Mark scheme

Autumn end-of-term			
Test A		**Test B**	
Q.	Marks	Q.	Marks
1	1	1	2
2	2	2	1
3	1	3	1
4	2	4	2
5	2	5	1
6	3	6	1
7	1	7	2
8	3	8	1
9	2		
10	2		
11	2		
12	1		
13	2		
14	1		
25 marks		*11 marks*	

Spring end-of-term			
Test A		**Test B**	
Q.	Marks	Q.	Marks
1	3	1	4
2	4	2	1
3	3	3	4
4	1	4	2
5	2	5	1
6	2	6	2
7	4	7	2
8	3		
9	3		
25 marks		*16 marks*	

Summer end-of-term			
Test A		**Test B**	
Q.	Marks	Q.	Marks
1	2	1	3
2	3	2	2
3	3	3	2
4	1	4	4
5	3	5	2
6	4	6	4
7	5	7	2
8	2	8	2
9	1	9	1
10	3	10	2
11	2		
12	4		
13	2		
14	1		
15	2		
16	2		
17	2		
18	2		
19	2		
46 marks		*24 marks*	

National Curriculum sub-levels

Autumn end-of-term	
Test A	
Marks	Sub-level
21+	2b or above
15–20	2c
9–14	1a
Test B	
Marks	Sub-level
7+	2b or above
If the child is working at below 1a, make a teacher assessment as to their NC level.	

Spring end-of-term	
Test A	
Marks	Sub-level
19+	2b or above
12–18	2c
8–11	1a
Test B	
Marks	Sub-level
8+	2a or above
If the child is working at below 1a, make a teacher assessment as to their NC level.	

Summer end-of-term	
Test A	
Marks	Sub-level
33+	3c or above
24–32	2a
16–23	2b
9–15	2c
Test B	
Marks	Sub-level
11+	3c or above
If the child is working at below 2c, make a teacher assessment as to their NC level.	

Class Records and Resources

Year 2 Autumn • Mental

Class achievement record

Objectives	Q. no.	Pupils' names									
Read and write numbers up to 100 in figures	1										
Rehearse addition and subtraction facts for pairs of numbers that total 10	2										
Know by heart doubles for numbers up to at least 15 and corresponding halves	3										
Solve 'real-life' problems involving money (paying an exact sum)	4										
Add three numbers by putting the largest number first	5										
Use the names of common 2D shapes, including: pentagon, hexagon, octagon	6										
Know what each digit in a 2-digit number represents, including 0 as a place holder	7										
Estimate, measure and compare lengths using standard units: centimetres	8										
Begin to halve multiples of 10 up to 100	9										
Order numbers up to at least 100	10										

Year 2 Spring • Mental

Class achievement record

Objectives	Q. no.	Pupils' names									
Rehearse addition and subtraction facts for pairs of numbers that total up to 10	1										
Count on in 2s, 5s or 10s up to 100	2										
Subtract a multiple of 10 from a 2-digit number by counting back in 10s	3										
Count on and back in 1s or 10s from a 2-digit number	4										
Count on and back in 100s from a multiple of 100	5										
Begin to recognise odd and even numbers up to at least 50	6										
Introduce multiplication as 'lots of'	7										
Say a number lying between two numbers, up to at least 100	8										
Begin to understand division as grouping	9										
Add and subtract 9 and 11 by adding and subtracting 10	10										

Year 2 Summer • Mental

Class achievement record

Objectives	Q. no.	Pupils' names									
Find the difference between two numbers by counting on	1										
Know by heart pairs of multiples of 10 that total 100	2										
Read a simple capacity scale to the nearest labelled and unlabelled division	3										
Know by heart the multiplication facts for 2, 5 and 10 times-tables	4										
Begin to recognise halves and quarters of small numbers of objects	5										
Begin to partition 3-digit numbers into H, T and U	6										
Double multiples of 5 up to 50	7										
Begin to understand multiplication as repeated addition or as describing an array	8										
Begin to round numbers less than 100 to the nearest 10	9										
Begin to recognise halves and quarters of small numbers of shapes	10										

Year 2 Autumn half-term • Written A

Class achievement record

Objectives	Q. no.	Pupils' names									
Read and write numbers up to 100 in figures	1										
Count on and back in 1s or 10s from a 2-digit number	2										
Begin to count up to 100 objects by grouping in 5s or 10s	3										
Partition 2-digit numbers into T and U	4										
Order numbers up to at least 100 and position them on a 100-square	5										
Add by counting on in 1s from the larger number, crossing a multiple of 10	6										
Rehearse addition and subtraction facts for pairs of numbers that total up to 9	7, 8										
Rehearse addition and subtraction facts for pairs of numbers that total 10	9										

Year 2 Autumn half-term • Written B

Class achievement record

Objectives	Q. no.	Pupils' names									
Begin to count up to 100 objects by grouping in 5s or 10s	1										
Partition 2-digit numbers into T and U	2										
Order numbers up to at least 100 and position them on a 100-square	3										
Add by counting on in 1s from the larger number, crossing a multiple of 10	4, 5										
Add three numbers by putting the largest number first	6										
Rehearse addition and subtraction facts for pairs of numbers that total up to 10	7										

Year 2 Spring half-term • Written A

Class achievement record

Objectives	Q. no.	Pupils' names									
Count on and back in 100s from a multiple of 100	1										
Count on and back in 1s or 10s from a 2-digit or 3-digit number	2, 5										
Count on in 2s (revise)	3										
Begin to recognise odd and even numbers up to at least 50	4										
Compare two or more 2-digit numbers	6a, b										
Say a number lying between two numbers, up to at least 100	6c										
Rehearse addition and subtraction facts for pairs of numbers that total up to 10	7, 8										
Know that a right angle is a measure of a quarter turn	9										
Recognise right angles in simple shapes	10										
Recognise whole, half and quarter turns; recognise clockwise and anticlockwise turns	11a										
Recognise clockwise and anticlockwise turns; know that a right angle is a measure of a quarter turn	11b										

Year 2 Spring half-term • Written B

Class achievement record

Objectives	Q. no.	Pupils' names									
Count on and back in 1s or 10s from a 2-digit or 3-digit number; count on and back in 100s from a multiple of 100	1										
Begin to recognise odd and even numbers up to at least 50	2										
Count on and back in 1s or 10s from a 2-digit or 3-digit number	3										
Compare two or more 2-digit numbers	4										
Rehearse addition and subtraction facts for pairs of numbers that total up to 10	5										
Know that a right angle is a measure of a quarter turn; recognise clockwise and anticlockwise turns	6, 7										

Year 2 Summer half-term • Written A

Class achievement record

Objectives	Q. no.	Pupils' names									
Read and write numbers up to 100 in words	1										
Begin to partition 3-digit numbers into H, T and U	2										
Begin to round numbers less than 100 to the nearest 10	3										
Add a 1-digit number to a 2-digit number, crossing a multiple of 10	4										
Find the difference between two numbers, by counting on	5										
Begin to recognise halves and quarters of small numbers of objects	6, 7										
Begin to recognise halves and quarters of shapes	8										
Know by heart pairs of multiples of 10 that total 100	9										
Know by heart addition and subtraction facts for pairs of numbers that total up to 10	10a, b										
Know by heart addition and subtraction facts for pairs of numbers that total 20	10c, d										
Use pairs that total 10 to make the next multiple of 10	11										
Know by heart addition and subtraction facts for pairs of numbers that total 20	12										

Year 2 Summer half-term • Written B

Class achievement record

Objectives	Q. no.	Pupils' names									
Begin to partition 3-digit numbers into H, T and U	1										
Add a 1-digit number to a 2-digit number, crossing a multiple of 10	2										
Find the difference between two numbers by counting on	3										
Begin to recognise halves and quarters of small numbers of objects	4										
Begin to recognise halves and quarters of shapes	5										
Know by heart pairs of multiples of 10 that total 100	6										
Use pairs that total 10 to make the next multiple of 10	7										

Year 2 Autumn end-of-term • Written A Class achievement record

Objectives	Q. no.	Pupils' names									
Use units of time and know the relationship between them: months in a year, seasons in a year	1										
Know what each digit in a 2-digit number represents, including 0 as a place holder	2										
Use the names of common 2D shapes, including: pentagon, hexagon, octagon	3										
Partition 2-digit numbers into T and U	4										
Rehearse addition and subtraction facts for pairs of numbers that total 10	5										
Begin to recognise line symmetry	6										
Order numbers up to at least 100 and position them on a 100-square	7										
Extend understanding of subtraction as taking away	8										
Know by heart doubles for numbers up to at least 15 and corresponding halves	9										
Recognise halving as the inverse of doubling; Know by heart doubles for numbers up to at least 15 and corresponding halves	10										
Add by counting on in 1s from the larger number, crossing a multiple of 10	11a										
Add three numbers by putting the largest number first	11b										

Objectives	**Q. no.**	**Pupils' names**									
Use units of time and know the relationship between them: hours in a day, days in a week	12										
Sort 2D shapes and describe their features: number of sides and corners	13										
Count back in 1s, crossing a multiple of ten, beginning to partition	14										

Year 2 Autumn end-of-term • Written B

Class achievement record

Objectives	Q. no.	Pupils' names									
Partition 2-digit numbers into T and U	1										
Count on and back in 1s or 10s from a 2-digit number	2										
Order numbers up to at least 100 and position them on a 100-square	3										
Sort 2D shapes and describe their features: number of sides and corners	4										
Know what each digit in a 2-digit number represents, including 0 as a place holder; Know by heart doubles for numbers up to at least 15 and corresponding halves	5										
Begin to sketch the reflection of a simple shape in a mirror line	6										
Rehearse addition and subtraction facts for pairs of numbers that total 10	7										
Count back in 1s, crossing a multiple of ten, beginning to partition	8										

Class achievement record

Objectives	Q. no.	Pupils' names									
Introduce multiplication as 'lots of'	1, 3										
Count on and back in 1s or 10s from a 2- or 3-digit number	2, 5										
Rehearse addition and subtraction facts for pairs of numbers that total up to 9	4										
Begin to add and subtract 19 and 21 by adding and subtracting 20	6										
Use the names of common 3D shapes, including: cube, cuboid, cylinder, sphere, cone	7a										
Sort 3D shapes and describe their features: number of faces and corners	7b, c, d										
Sort, organise and interpret information in a pictogram	8										
Count on in 2s, 5s or 10s up to 100	9										

Year 2 Spring end-of-term • Written B

Class achievement record

Objectives	Q. no.	Pupils' names									
Introduce multiplication as 'lots of'	1										
Begin to recognise odd and even numbers up to at least 100	2										
Count on or back in 1s or 10s from a 2- or 3-digit number	3										
Begin to derive doubles of multiples of 5 up to 100 and the corresponding halves	4										
Subtract a multiple of 10 from a 2-digit number by counting back in 10s	5										
Sort 3D shapes and describe their features: number of faces and corners	6										
Begin to add and subtract 19 and 21 by adding and subtracting 20	7a, b										

Year 2 Summer end-of-term • Written A

Class achievement record

Objectives	Q. no.	Pupils' names									
Add by identifying near doubles for multiples of 5	1										
Know by heart the multiplication facts for 2, 5 and 10 times-tables	2										
Begin to round numbers less than 100 to the nearest 10	3										
Know by heart doubles for numbers up to at least 15 and the corresponding halves	4										
Read the time to the quarter hour on analogue and 12-hour digital clocks	5										
Know by heart addition and subtraction facts for pairs of numbers that total up to 10	6a, b										
Know by heart addition and subtraction facts for pairs of numbers that total 20	6c, d										
Count on and back in 1s or 10s from a 2- or 3-digit number	7a–d, 15										
Order numbers up to at least 100 and position them on a 100-square	7e										
Find the difference between two numbers by counting on	8										
Begin to recognise line symmetry	9										
Interpret information from a table	10										

Objectives	Q. no.	Pupils' names									
Understand that subtraction is the inverse of addition, using missing number sentences	11										
Begin to understand division as the inverse of multiplication	12										
Add two 2-digit numbers using an appropriate strategy	13										
Give instructions for moving along a route in straight lines and round corners	14										
Begin to add and subtract 19 and 21 by adding and subtracting 20	15, 16										
Find totals of sets of coins: relate to adding three or more numbers	17										
Add and begin to subtract a 1-digit number to and from multiples of 10 and 100	18										
Use units of time and know the relationship between them: hours, minutes, seconds	19										

Year 2 Summer end-of-term • Written B

Class achievement record

Objectives	Q. no.	Pupils' names									
Know by heart the multiplication facts for 2, 5 and 10 times-tables	1										
Know by heart addition and subtraction facts for pairs of numbers that total 20; Begin to add three 1-digit numbers mentally	2										
Add a 1-digit to a 2-digit number, crossing a multiple of 10 (rehearse)	3										
Subtract one 2-digit number from another using an appropriate strategy	4										
Know by heart doubles for numbers up to at least 15 and corresponding halves; Double multiples of 5 up to 50; Halve multiples of 10 up to 100	5										
Begin to understand division as the inverse of multiplication	6										
Understand that subtraction is the inverse of addition, using missing number sentences	7										
Recognise fraction notation; Begin to recognise halves and quarters of small numbers of objects	8										
Begin to recognise odd and even numbers up to at least 100; Say a number lying between two numbers, up to at least 100	9										
Find the difference between two numbers by counting on; Begin to add by bridging a multiple of 10 (36 + 8 = 36 + 4 + 4)	10										

Class Overview Sheet

Class: .... **Date:** ....

Name	Test Taken	Score	Level	Next Steps

Key issues for the class:

Next steps:

Name ....

Buying teddies

Name ....

Adding 3 single-digit numbers

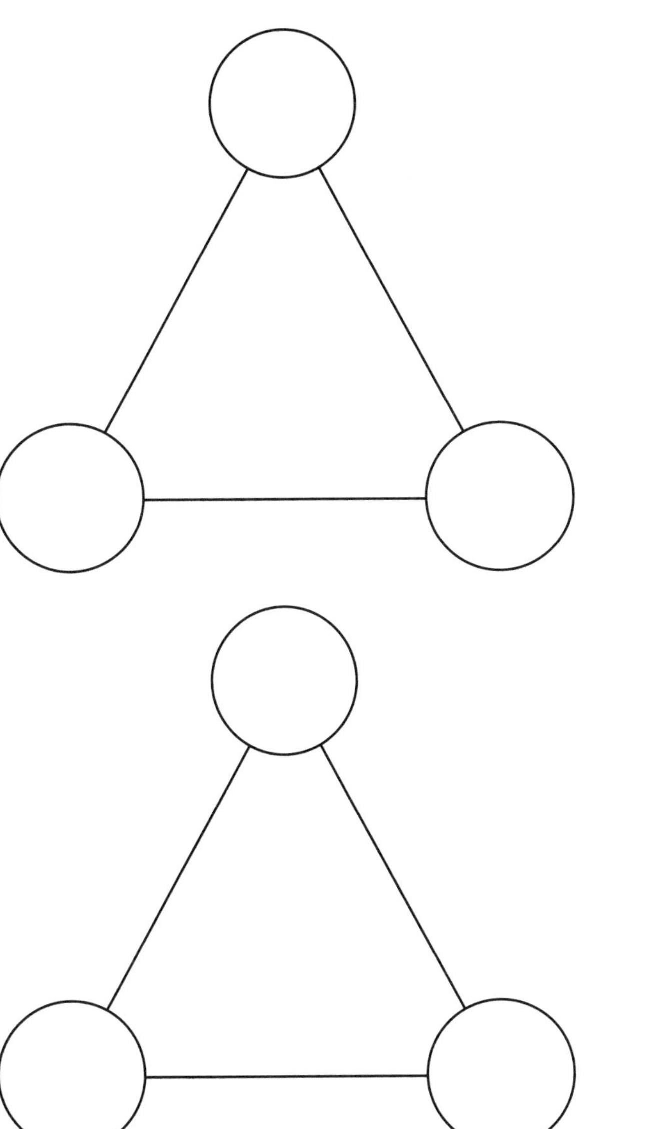

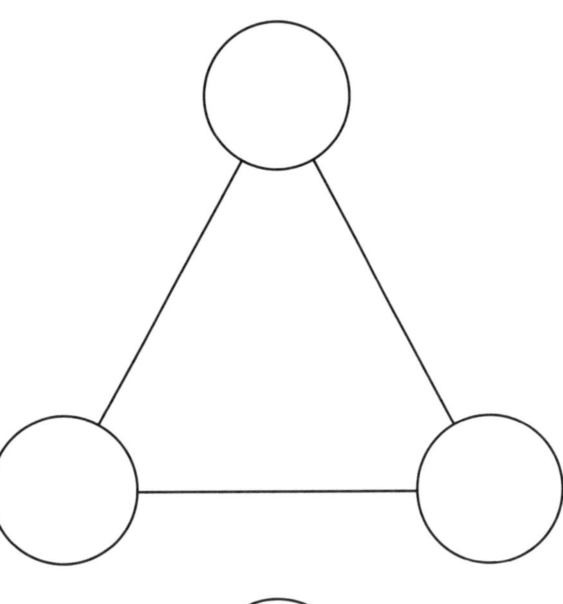

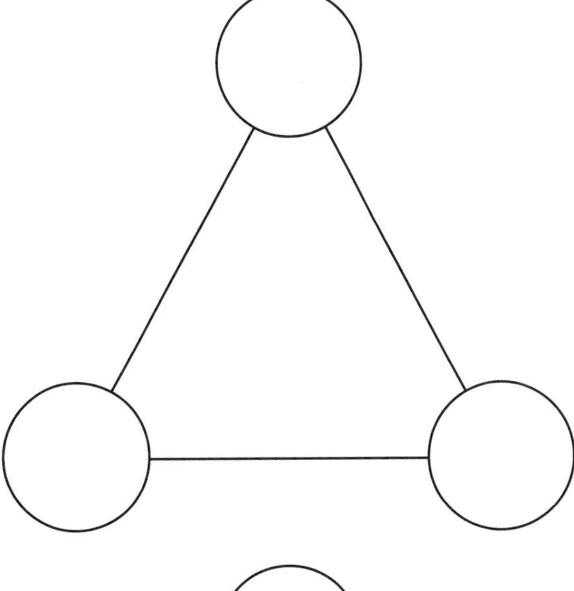

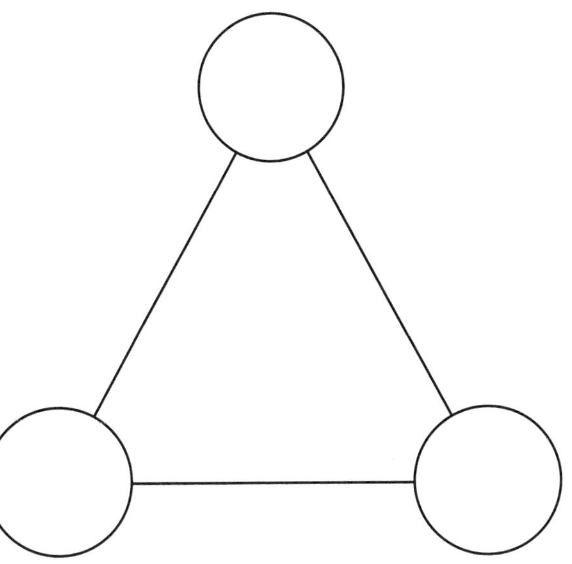

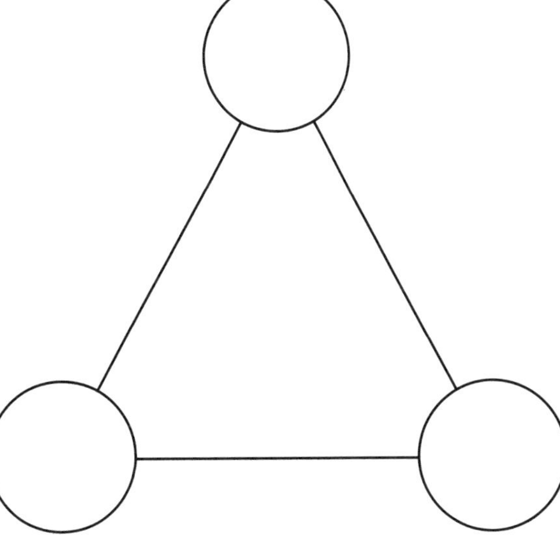

Name ....

Finding the right angles in shapes

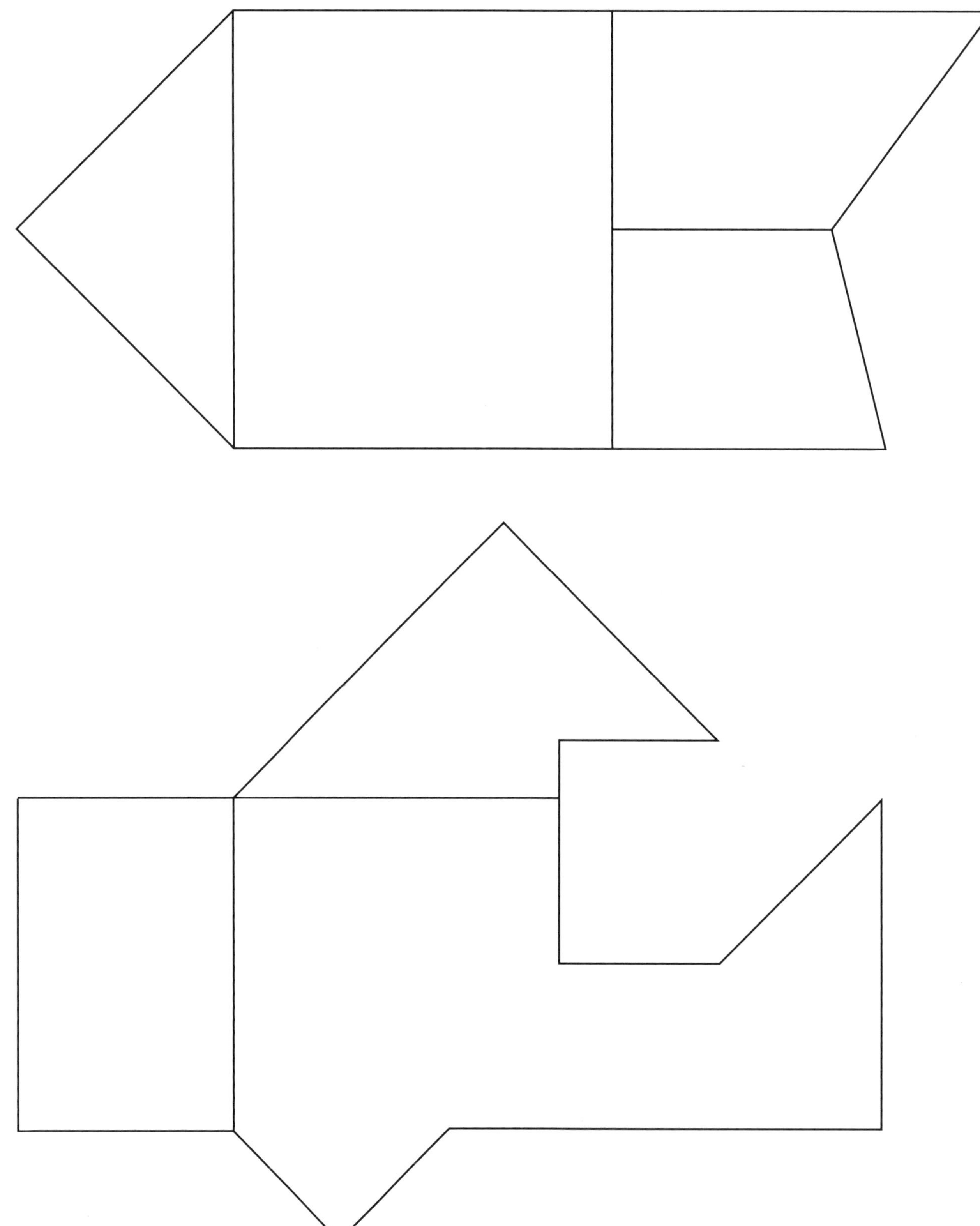

Name ....

Properties of shapes

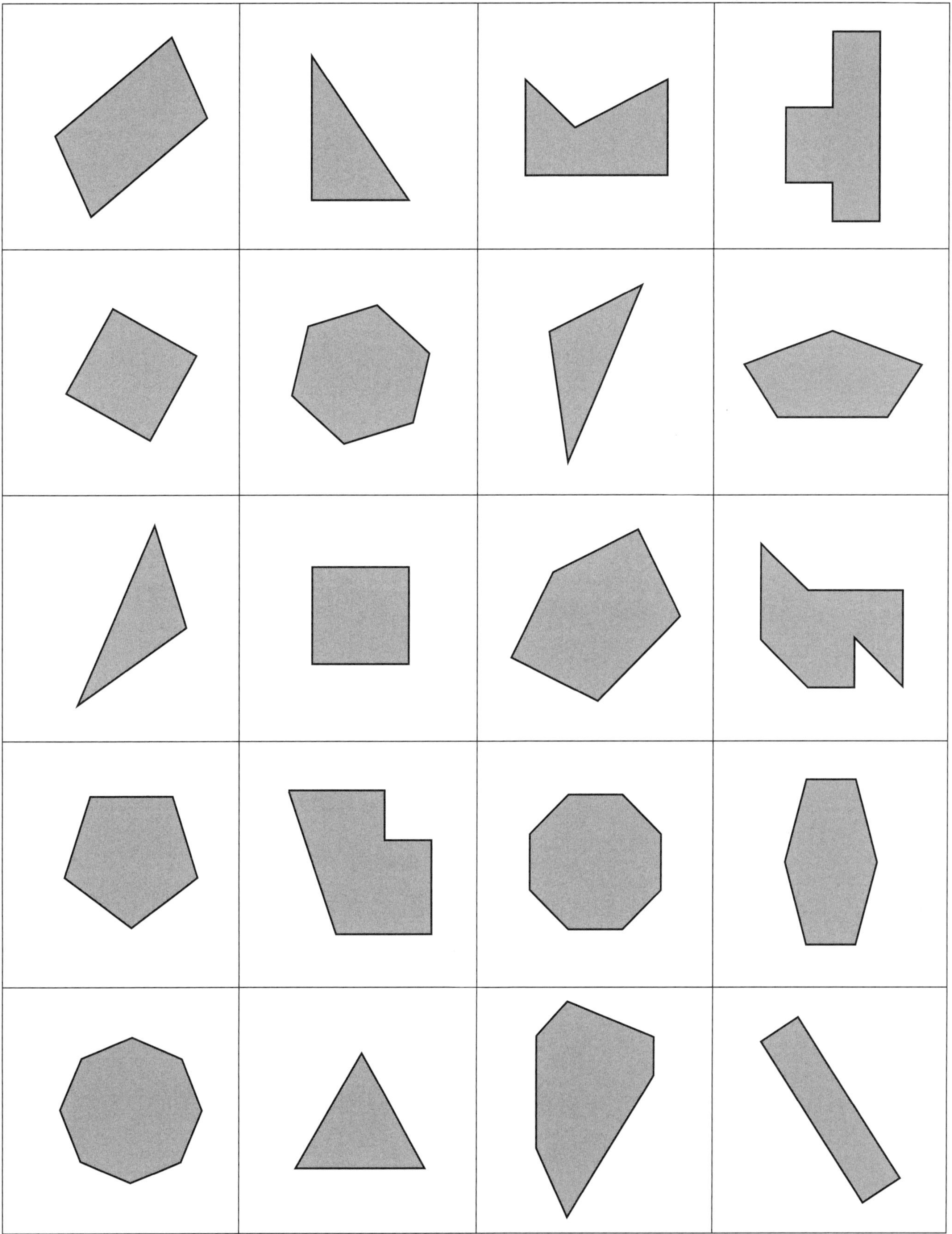

Name ....

Block graph

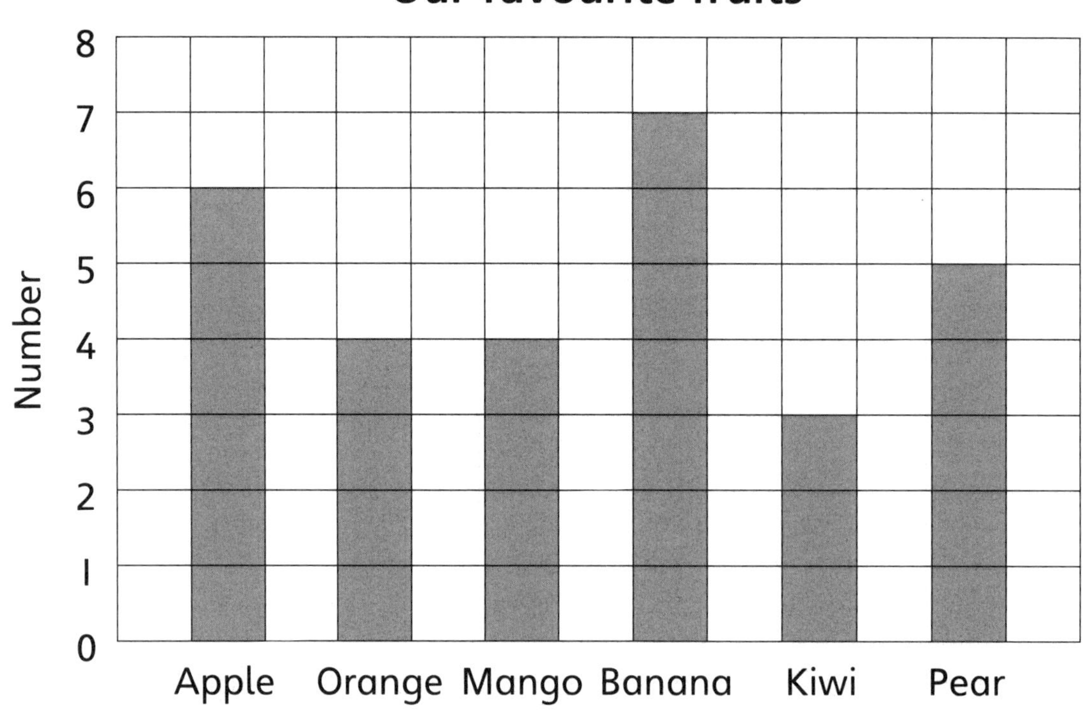

1 What is the most popular fruit?

2 What is the least popular fruit?

3 How many children chose Kiwi and Pear altogether?

4 How many children chose Apple and Banana altogether?

5 How many more children chose Banana than Mango?

6 How many fewer children chose Kiwi than Apple?

7 How many children in the class altogether?

8 Put the fruits in order from the least to most popular.

Name ....

Ordering cards

28 24 25

16 21 8

18 5 25

11 9 4

26 22 19

Write the three card numbers in order, smallest to largest

Name ....

Matching pairs

1	6	0	6
2	3	4	3
4	5	3	5
0	3	2	1

Colour pairs of numbers that make 6 to show they match.
Use a different colour for each pair.

Year 2: PCM R3

Name ....

Days and months

May

July

Monday

Saturday

November

Wednesday

June

September

October

February

Sunday

Friday

August

December

Thursday

January

April

March

Colour the days of the week in red, colour the months of the year in yellow.
Colour the month of your birthday in your favourite colour.

Name ....

Counting back

35 − 5 = ☐

42 − 2 = ☐

18 − 8 = ☐

89 − 9 = ☐

64 − 4 = ☐

24 − 4 = ☐

47 − 7 = ☐

12 − 2 = ☐

53 − 3 = ☐

76 − 6 = ☐

95 − 5 = ☐

68 − 8 = ☐

Complete the subtractions.

Name ....

Adding money

Write the amount in each purse.

Name ....

More and less

	1 more	1 less	10 more	10 less
14				
27				
31				
66				
52				
90				
35				
79				
42				
73				

Complete the table.

Year 2: PCM R7

Name ....

Hiding numbers

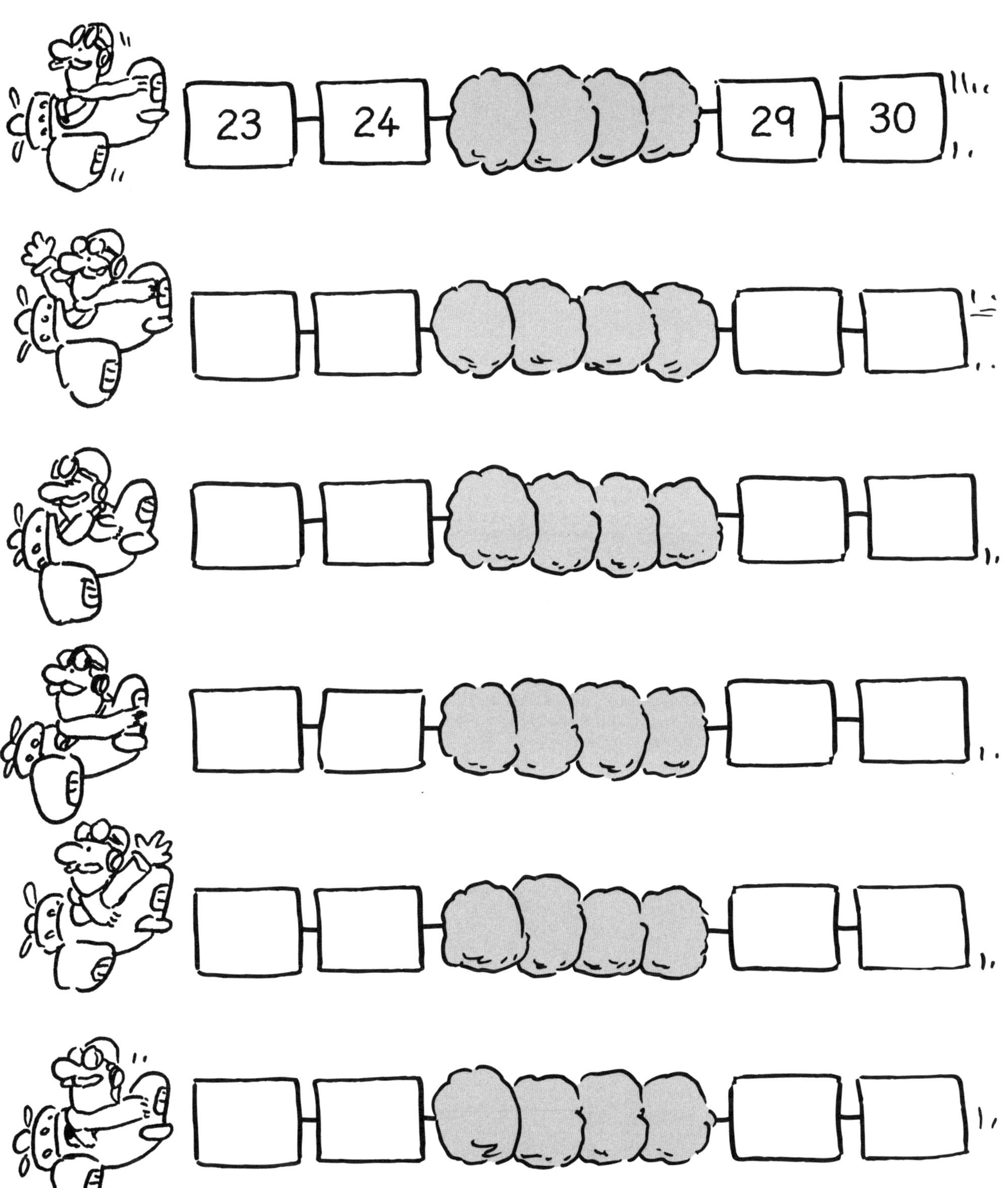

Write your own numbers in order. Hide four numbers behind the clouds.

Name ....

Dice throws

Number on dice	Number of throws
1	
2	
3	
4	
5	
6	

Work with a partner. Throw the dice and record the number of each type of throw using tally marks.

Name ....

Flat and solid shapes

Colour the solid shapes red. Colour the flat shapes blue.

Name ....

Taking away 10

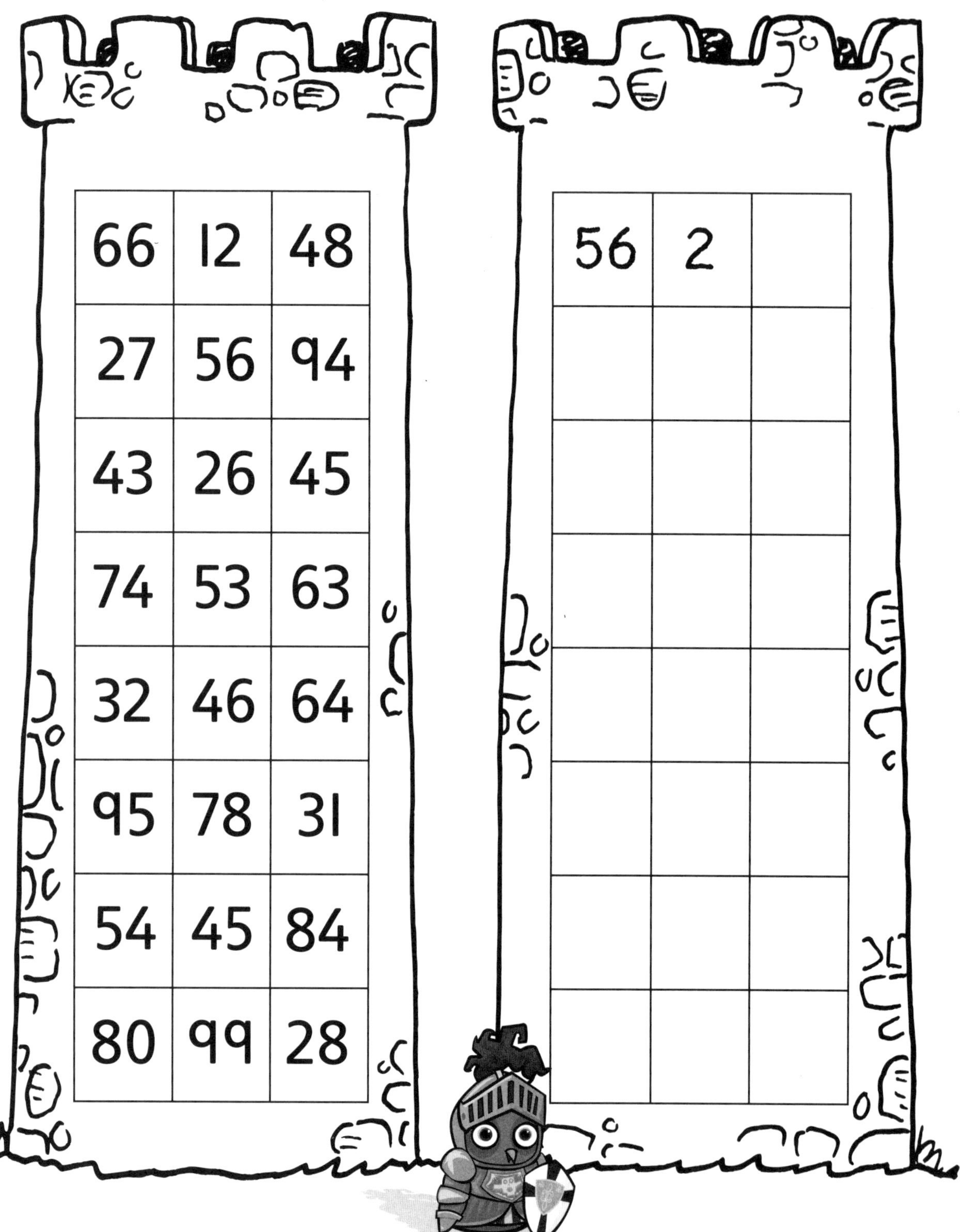

66	12	48
27	56	94
43	26	45
74	53	63
32	46	64
95	78	31
54	45	84
80	99	28

56	2	

Take away 10 from each number on the left-hand tower.
Write the answers in the matching squares on the right hand tower.

Name ....

Windows

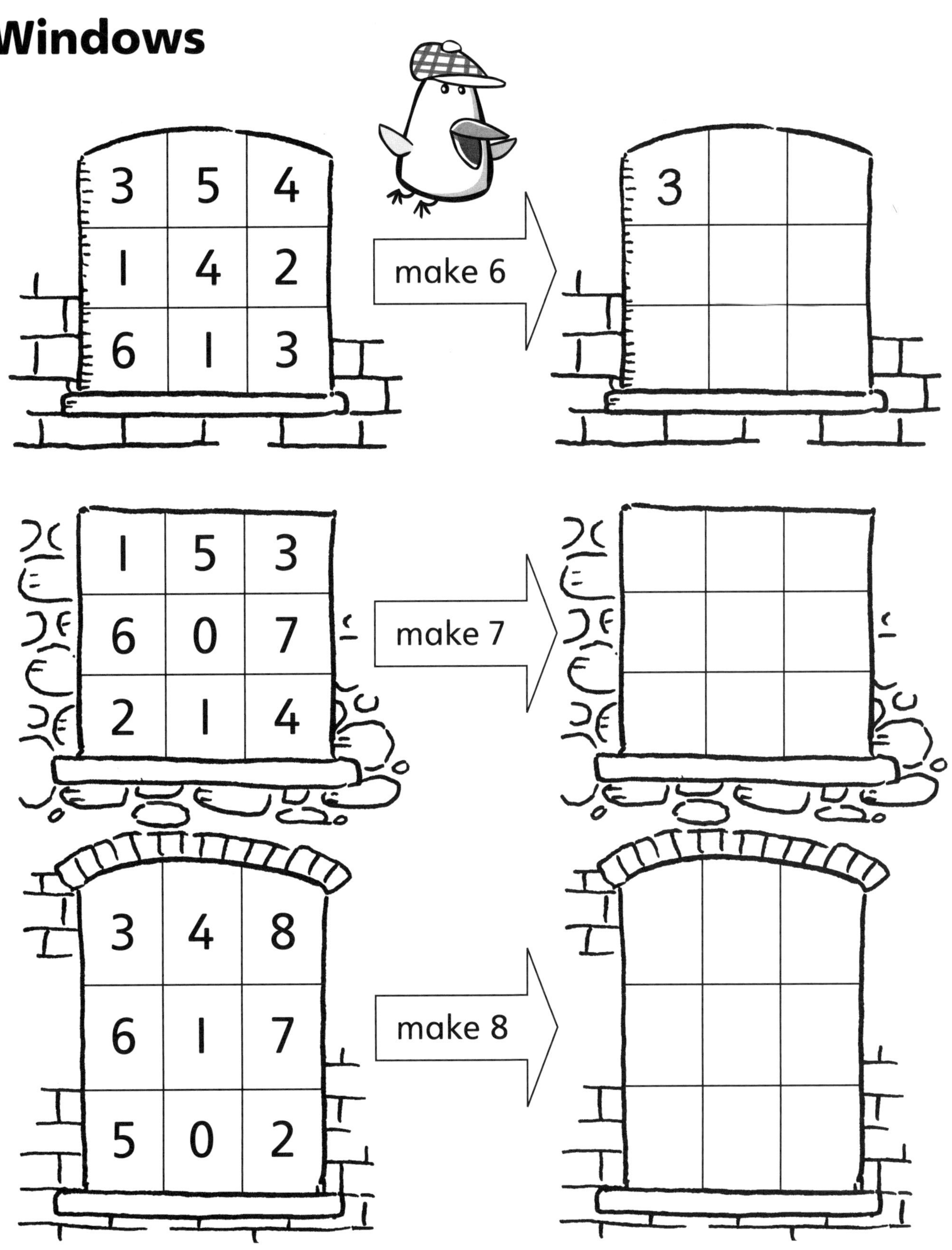

For each pair of windows, write numbers in the matching squares to make the totals shown on the arrows.

Name ....

Hours

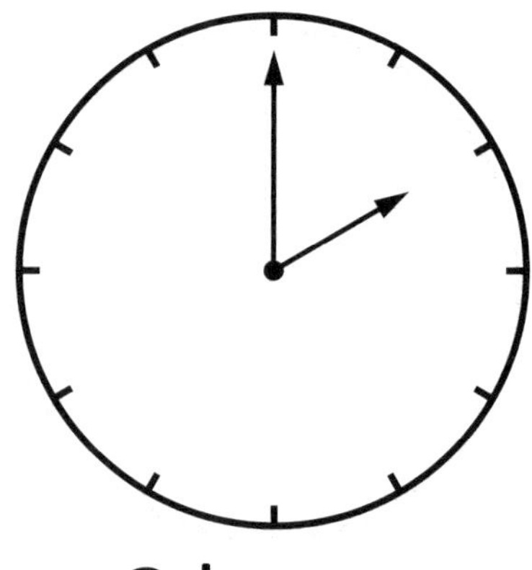

3 hours

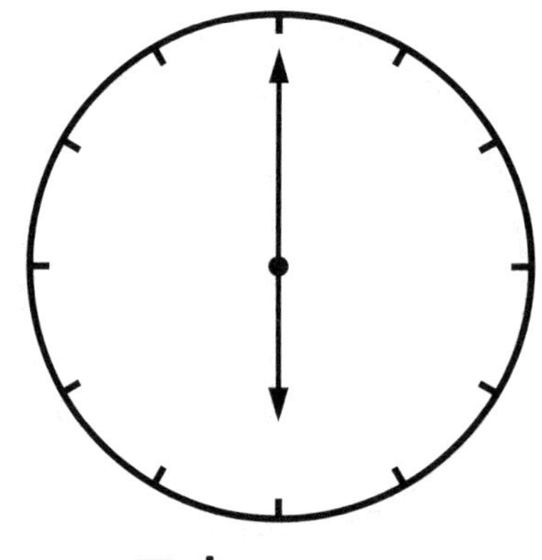

7 hours

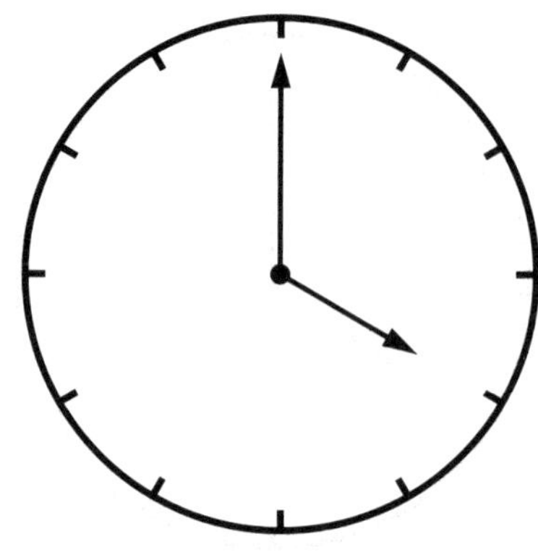

11 hours

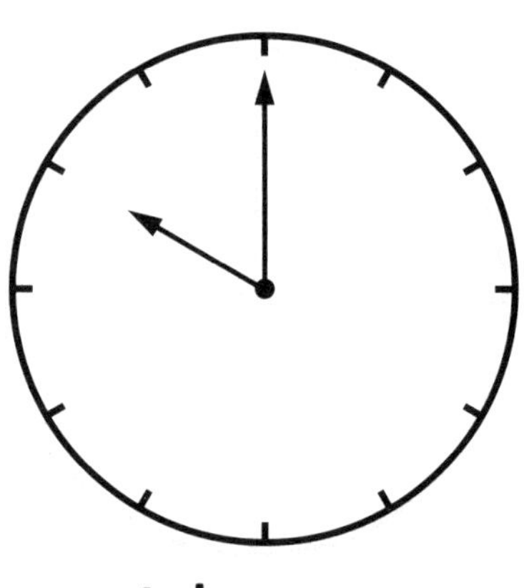

4 hours

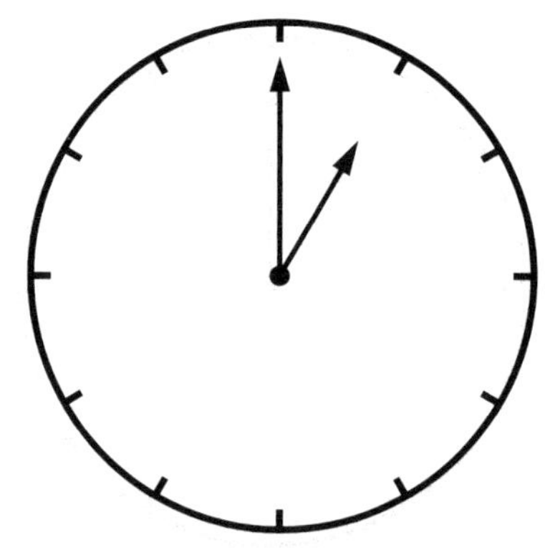

12 hours

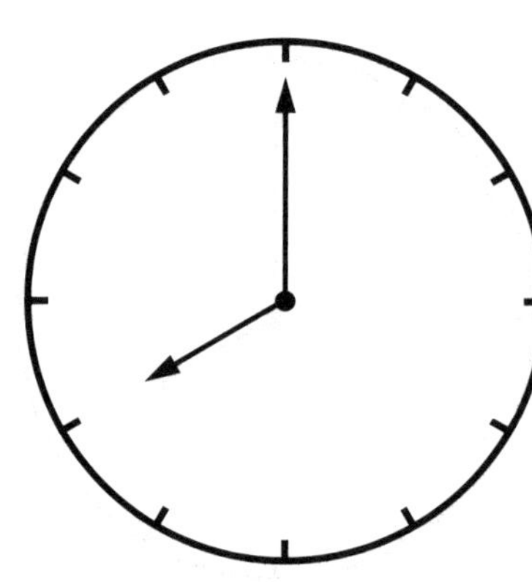

5 hours

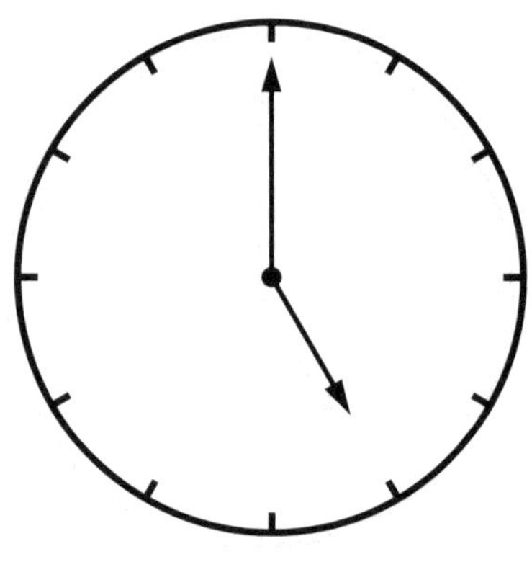

6 hours

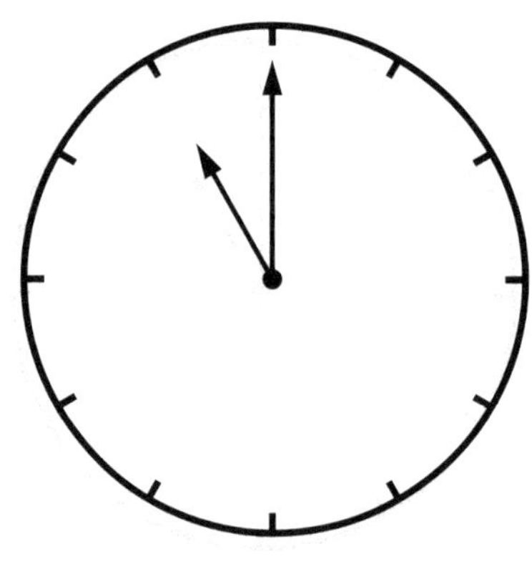

8 hours

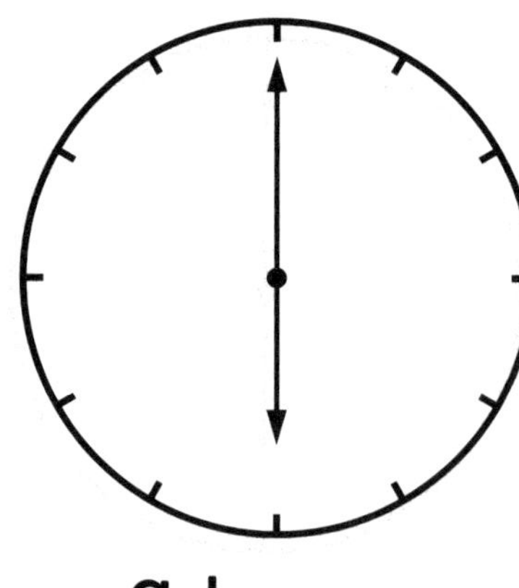

9 hours

Draw the position of the hour hand after these lengths of time.

Name ....

2s and 5s

start

1	2	3	4	5	6	7	8
16	15	14	13	12	11	10	9
17	18	19	20	21	22	23	24
32	31	30	29	28	27	26	25
33	34	35	36	37	38	39	40
48	47	46	45	44	43	42	41
49	50	51	52	53	54	55	56
64	63	62	61	60	59	58	57

finish

This is a game for two players. Start at 2 and colour all the twos in yellow. Start at 5 and colour all the fives in red. Each player places a counter at 'start'. Take turns to roll a dice and move your counter a matching number of spaces.
If you land on a yellow number, move to the next yellow number.
If you land on a red number, move to the next red number.
The winner is the first to reach 'finish'.

Year 2: Answers for Review PCMs

PCM R1

Ordering cards
2, 14, 23
6, 17, 29
7, 15, 18
24, 25, 28
8, 16, 21
5, 18, 25
4, 9, 11
19, 22, 26

PCM R2

Matching pairs
Combinations of:
1 and 5
2 and 4
3 and 3
6 and 0

PCM R3

Days and months
Red – Monday, Tuesday, Wednesday, Thursday, Friday, Saturday, Sunday
Yellow – January, February, March, April, May, June, July, August, September, October, November, December
Birthday month – colour will vary

PCM R4

Counting back
35 – 5 = 30
42 – 2 = 40
18 – 8 = 10
89 – 9 = 80
64 – 4 = 60
24 – 4 = 20
47 – 7 = 40
12 – 2 = 10
53 – 3 = 50
76 – 6 = 70
95 – 5 = 90
68 – 8 = 60

PCM R5

Adding money
50p + 20p = 70p
2p + 10p = 12p
5p + 10p = 15p
5p + 2p = 7p
£2 + £1 = £3
10p + 50p = 60p
20p + 1p = 21p
20p + 5p = 25p
50p + 5p = 55p
10p + 20p = 30p

PCM R6

More and less

	1 more	1 less	10 more	10 less
14	15	13	24	4
27	28	26	37	17
31	32	30	41	21
66	67	65	76	56
52	53	51	62	42
90	91	89	100	80
35	36	34	45	25
79	80	78	89	69
42	43	41	52	32
73	74	72	83	63

PCM R7

Hiding numbers
Answers will vary

PCM R8

Dice throws
Answers will vary

PCM R9

Flat and solid shapes

PCM R10

Taking away 10

56	2	38
17	46	84
33	16	35
64	43	53
22	36	54
85	68	21
44	35	74
70	89	18

PCM R11

Windows

3	1	2
5	2	4
0	5	3

6	2	4
1	7	0
5	6	3

5	4	0
2	7	1
3	8	6

PCM R12

Hours

Name ....

Tens and units

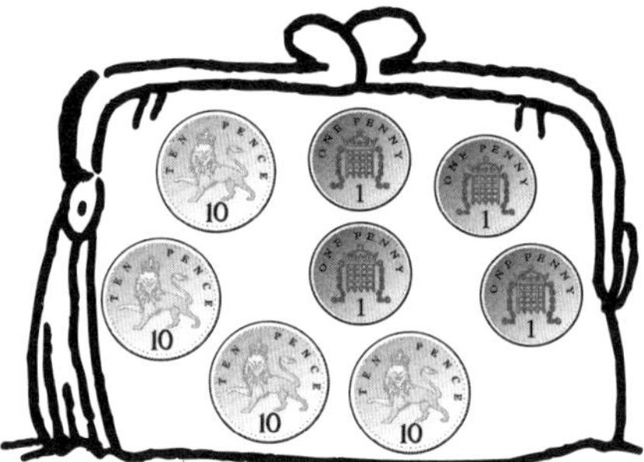

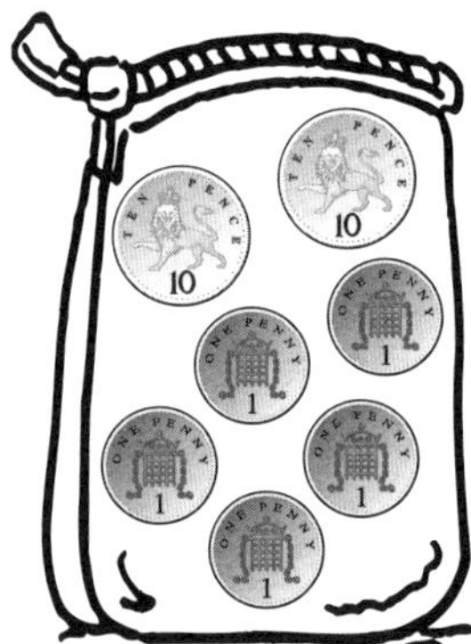

1	2	3	4	5	6	7	8	9	10
11	12	13	14	15	16	17	18	19	20
21	22	23	24	25	26	27	28	29	30
31	32	33	34	35	36	37	38	39	40
41	42	43	44	45	46	47	48	49	50
51	52	53	54	55	56	57	58	59	60
61	62	63	64	65	66	67	68	69	70
71	72	73	74	75	76	77	78	79	80
81	82	83	84	85	86	87	88	89	90
91	92	93	94	95	96	97	98	99	100

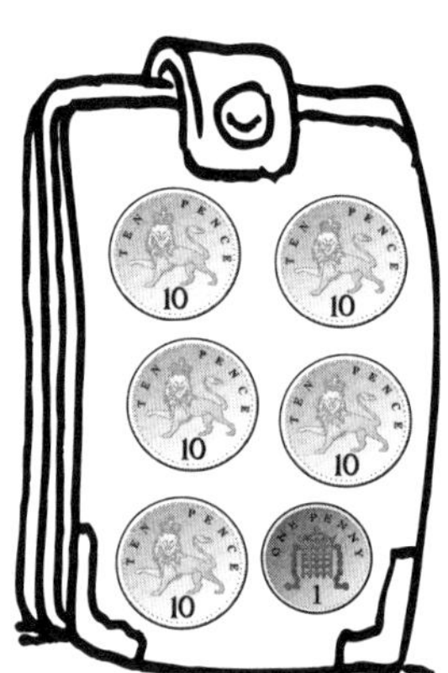

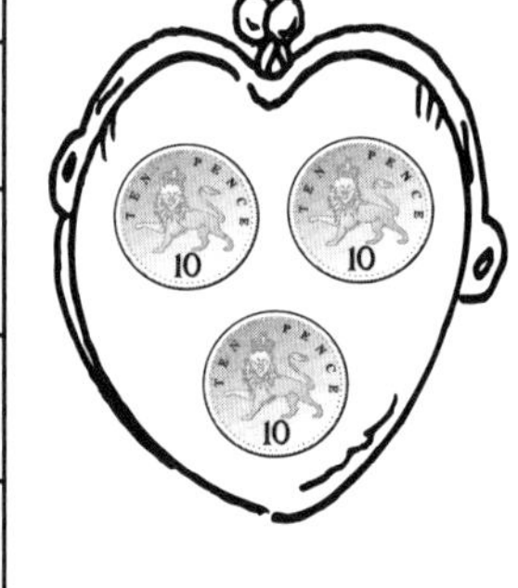
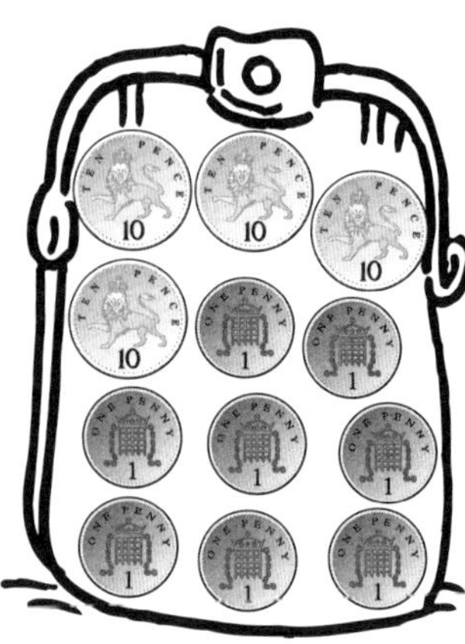
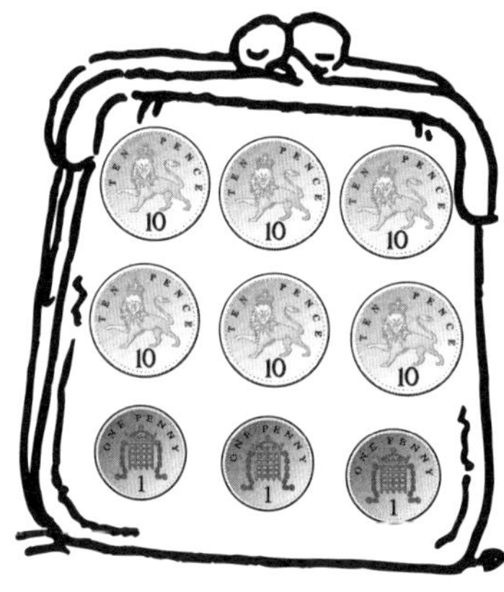

How much is in each purse? Colour the matching square on the grid.
Use a different colour for each purse.

PS

Name ....

Adding

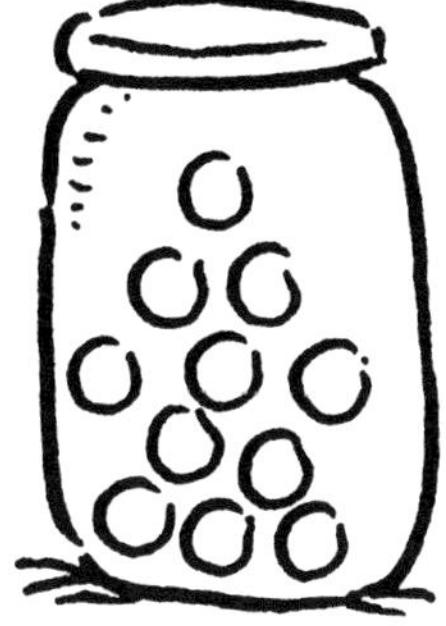

11 + 3 = ☐

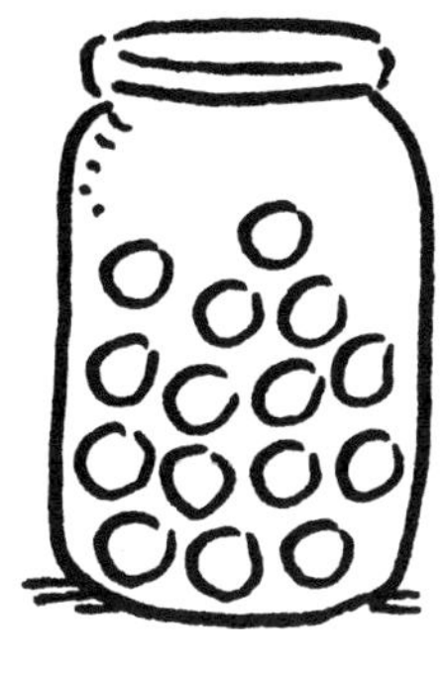

15 + 3 = ☐

13 + 4 = ☐

12 + 4 = ☐

14 + 5 = ☐

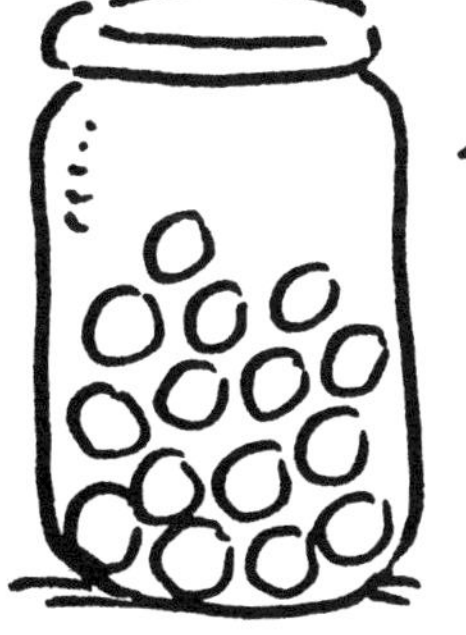

15 + 5 = ☐

11 + 6 = ☐

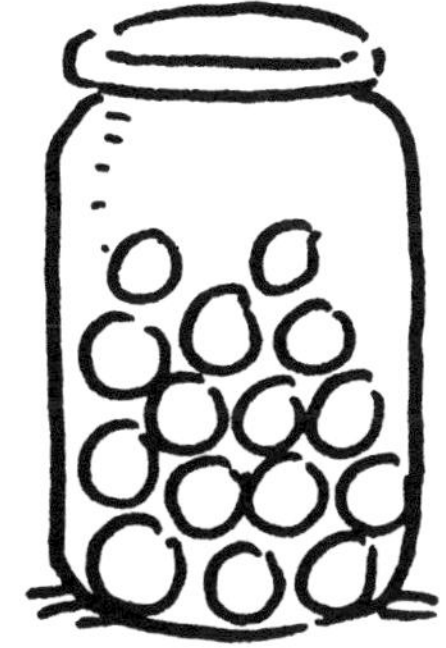

15 + 6 = ☐

How many marbles will be in each jar when the extra ones are added? Complete the additions.

PS

Name ....

Addition pairs

4 + ☐ = 7

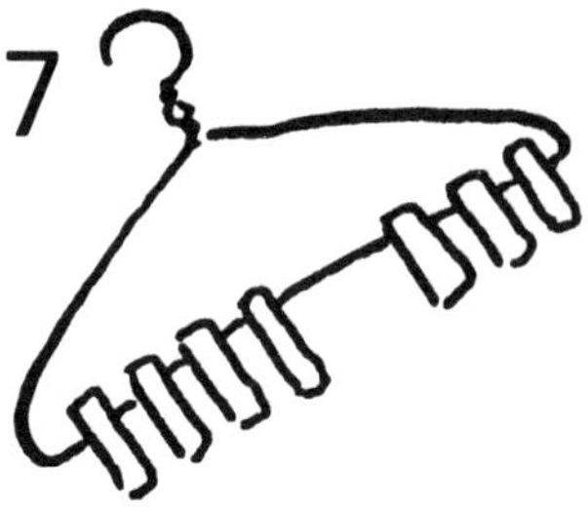

☐ + ☐ = 8

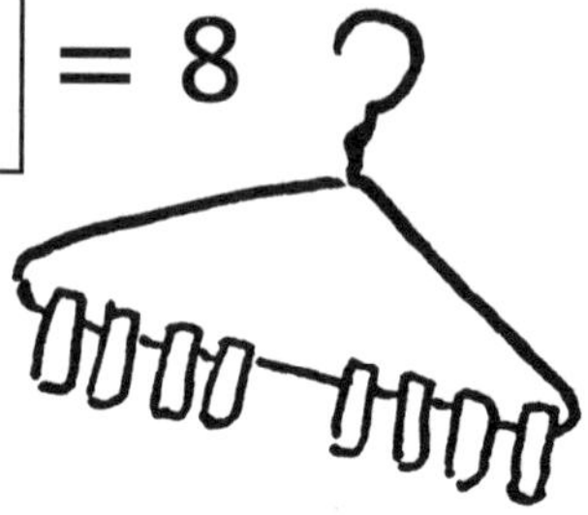

6 + ☐ = 7

5 + ☐ = 8

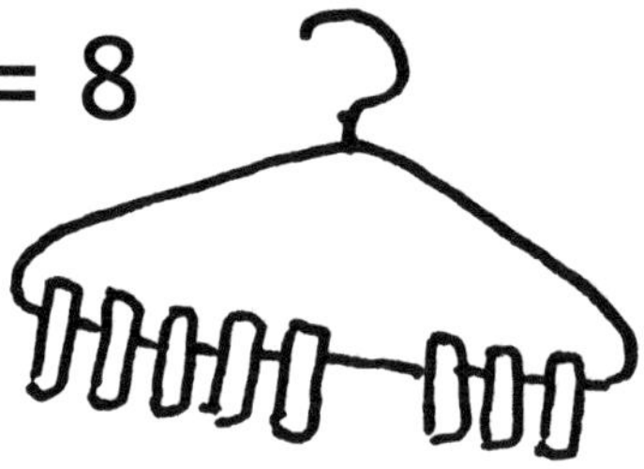

☐ + ☐ = 5

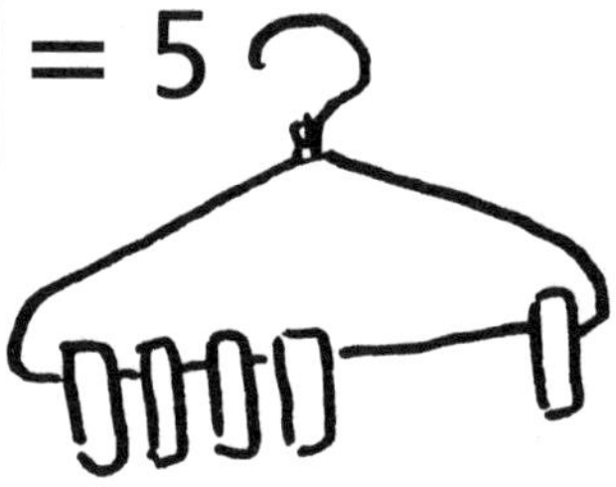

6 + ☐ = 8

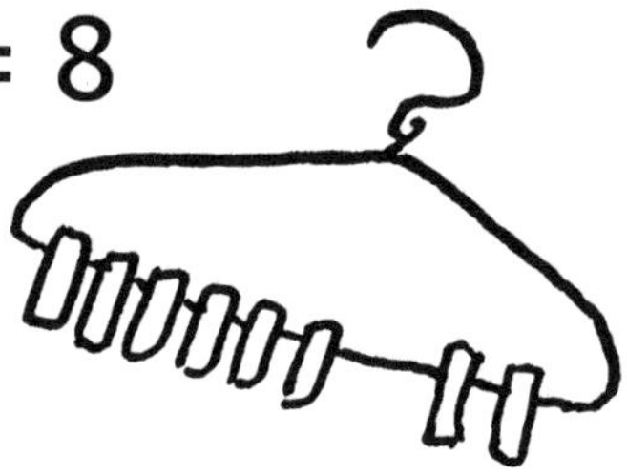

☐ + ☐ = 7

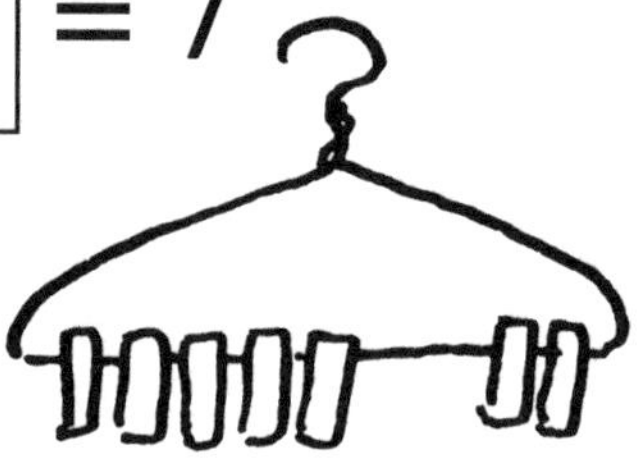

7 + ☐ = 8

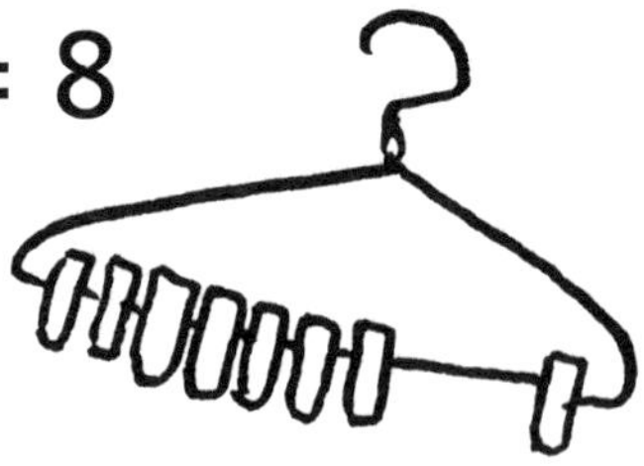

3 + ☐ = 5

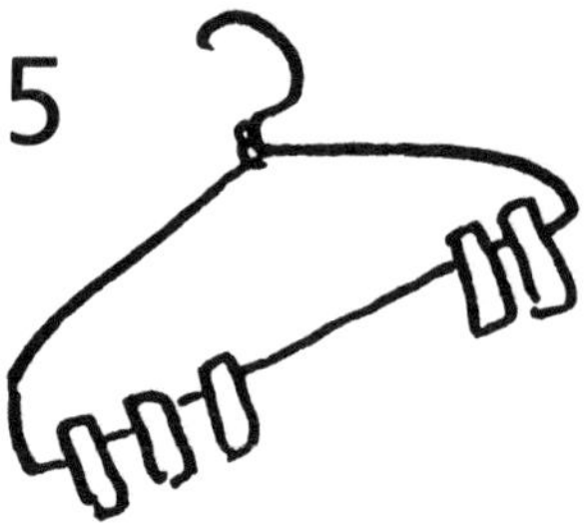

8 + ☐ = 8

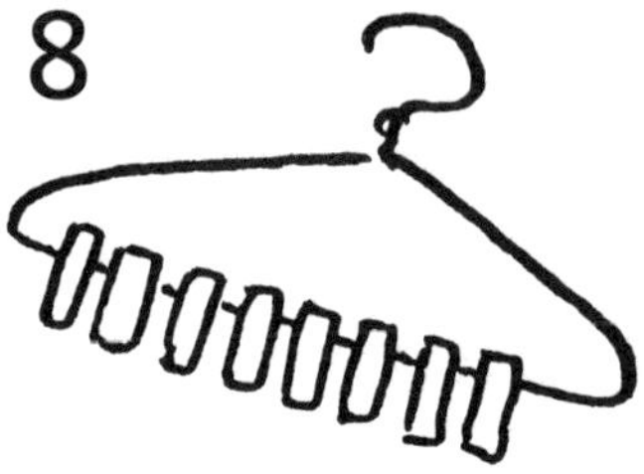

Complete the additions. Use a coat-hanger and pegs to help.

Year 2 • PCM 27

Name ....

Subtracting

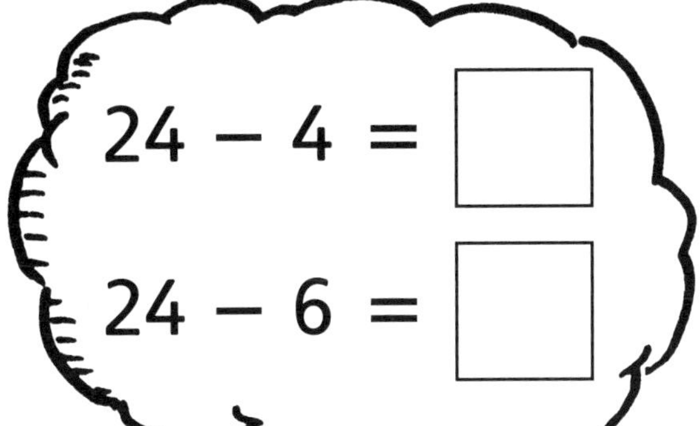

24 − 4 = ☐

24 − 6 = ☐

32 − 2 = ☐

32 − 5 = ☐

43 − 3 = ☐

43 − 5 = ☐

23 − 3 = ☐

23 − 6 = ☐

33 − 3 = ☐

33 − 7 = ☐

41 − 1 = ☐

41 − 4 = ☐

54 − 4 = ☐

54 − 7 = ☐

62 − 2 = ☐

62 − 5 = ☐

Complete the subtractions, crossing tens.

PS

Name ....

Halving game

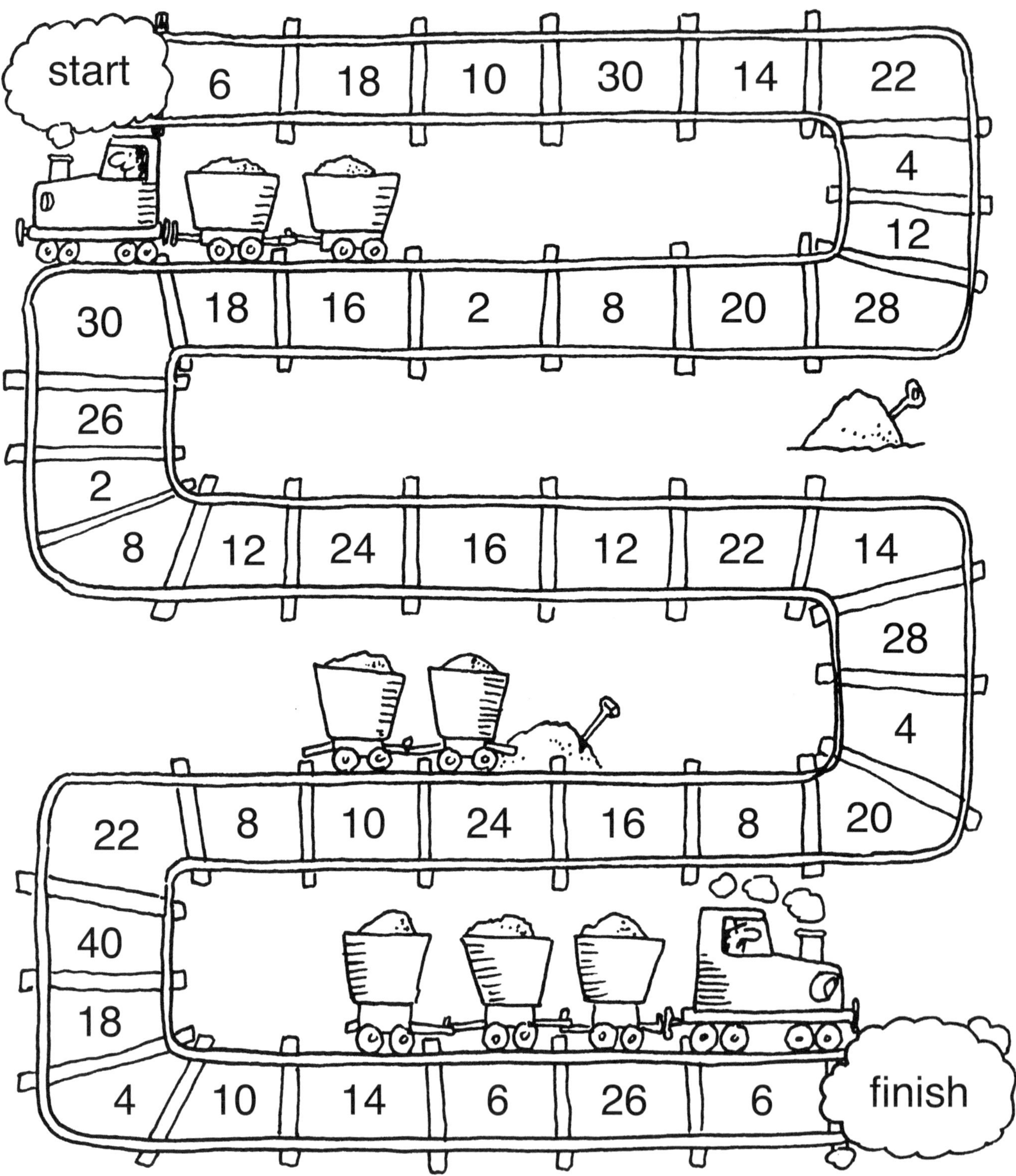

A game for two to four players, each with a counter at 'start'. Take turns to roll a dice, and move your counter a matching number of squares. Say half of the number you land on. If correct, move to the next space on the track. Check each other's answers. The winner is the first to reach or pass 'finish'.

Name ....

Scores

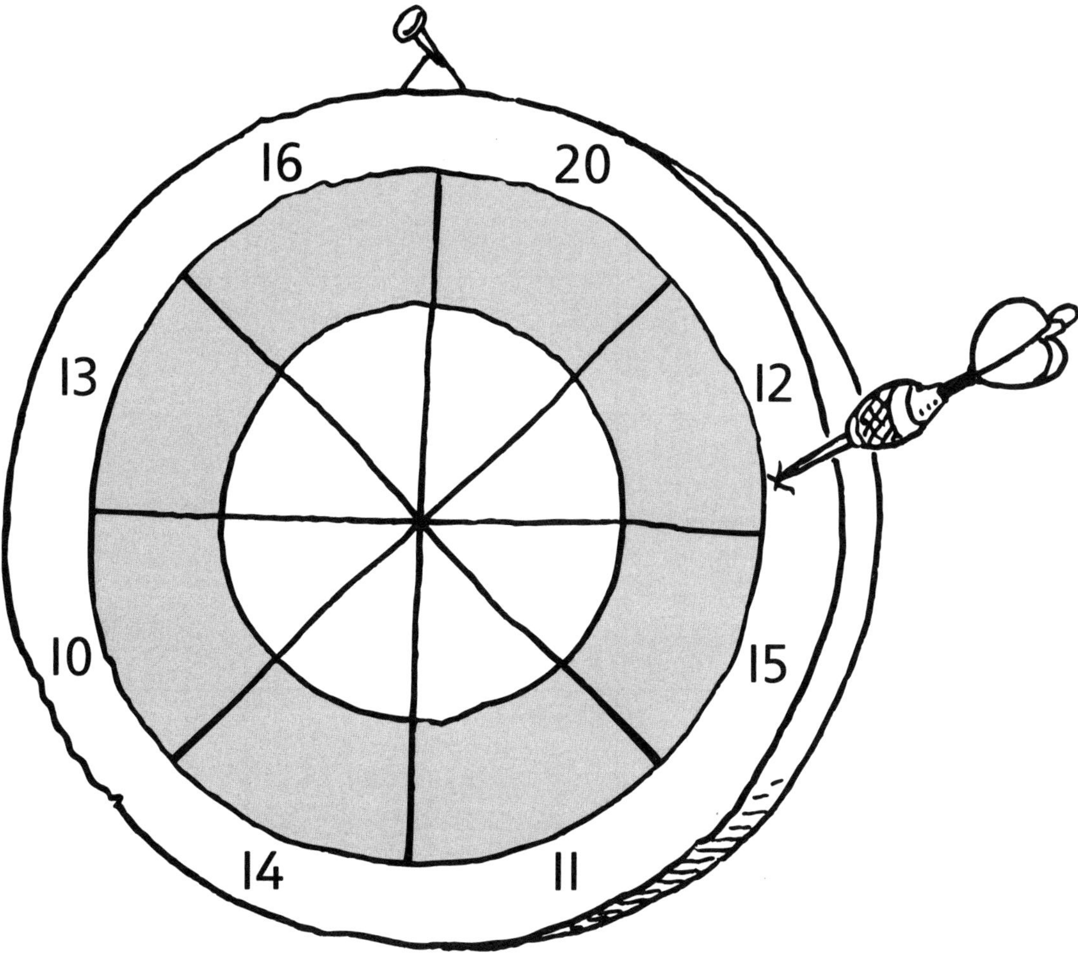

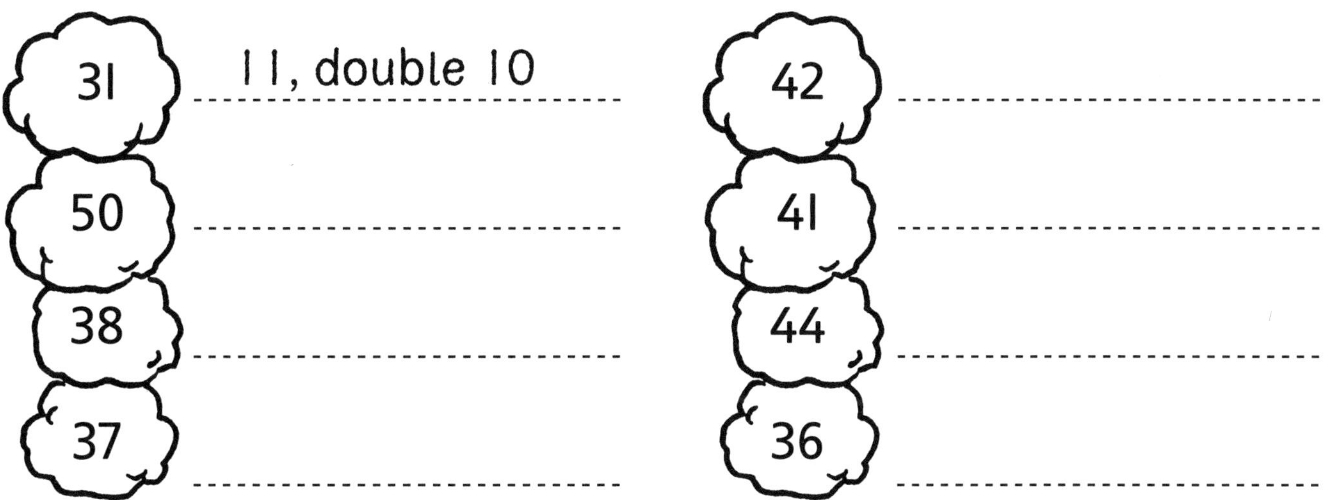

The grey ring counts double. Place two counters on the target to make the scores.
Write how you made them.
Find different ways of scoring 40 with two counters.

PS

Name ....

More and less

	1 more	1 less	10 more	10 less	100 more	100 less
11						
23						
38						
46						
87						
190						
131						
179						
142						
173						

Complete the table.

PS

Year 2 • PCM 60

Name ....

Corners

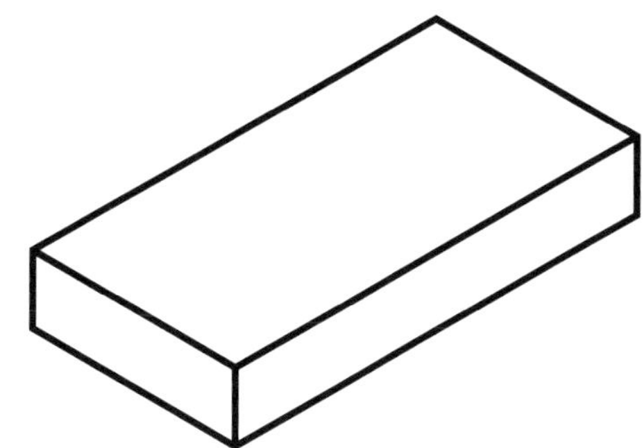

☐ corners

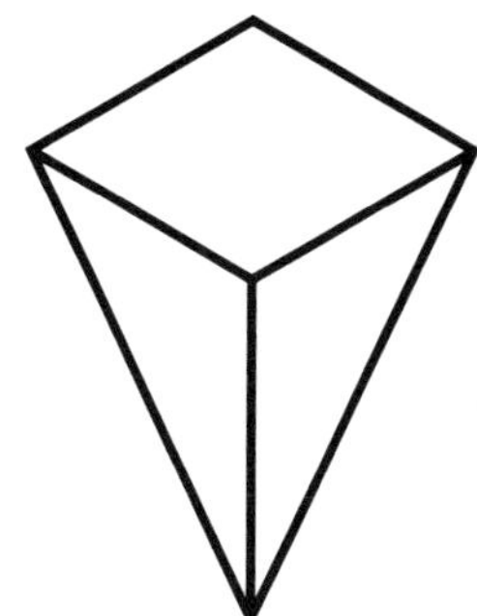

☐ corners

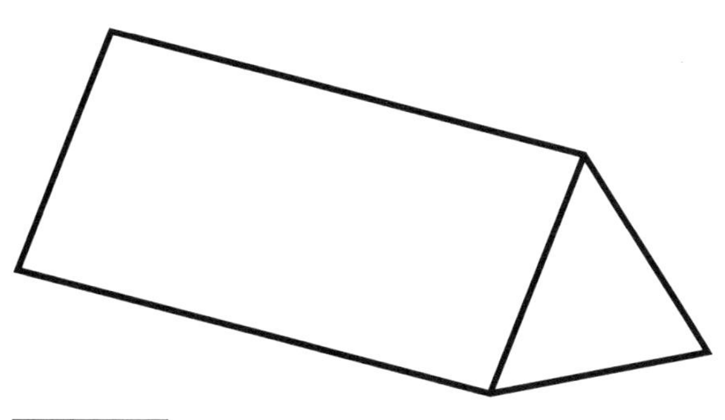

☐ corners

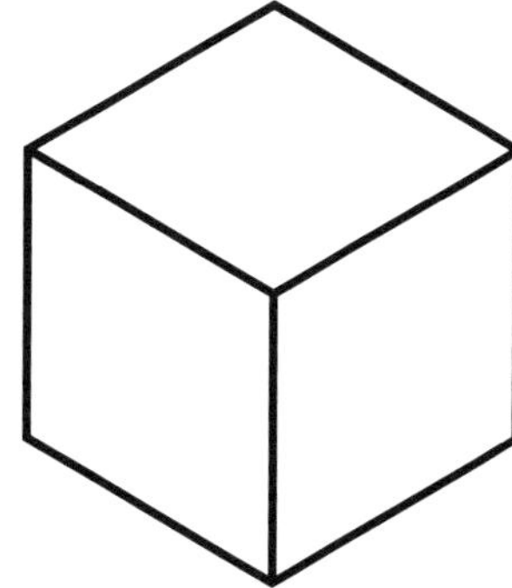

☐ corners

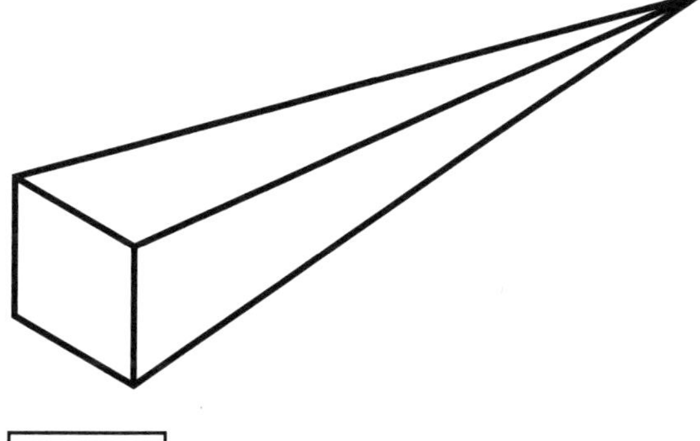

☐ corners

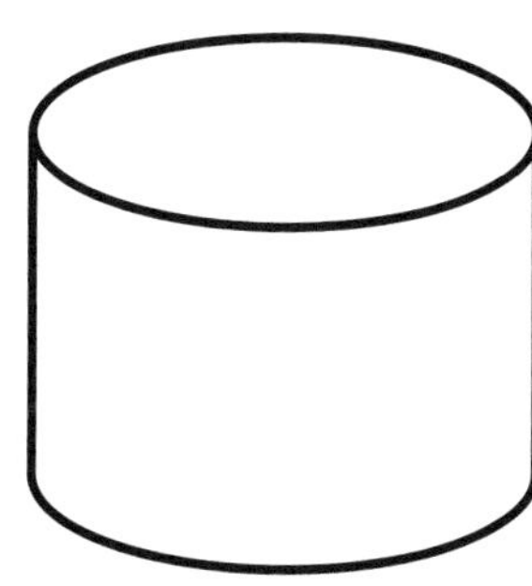

☐ corners

Find one of each shape. Write the number of corners each shape has.

PS

Name ....

Faces

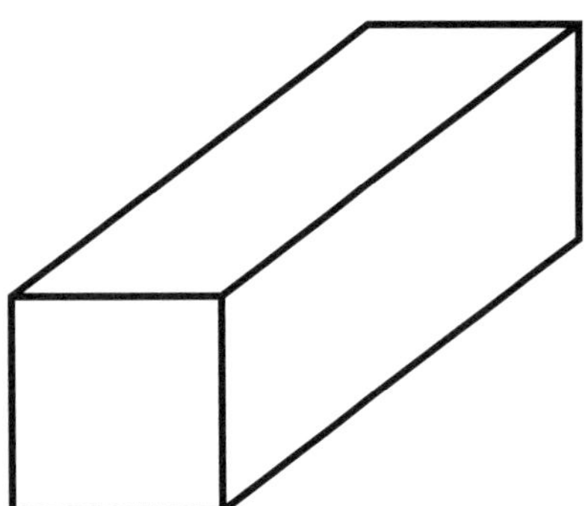

2 squares

4 rectangles

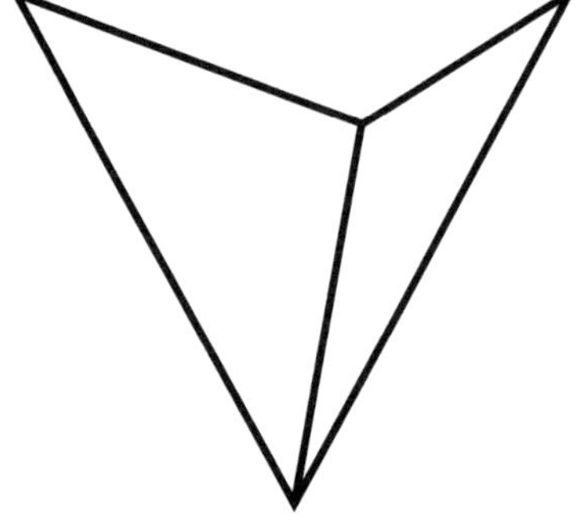

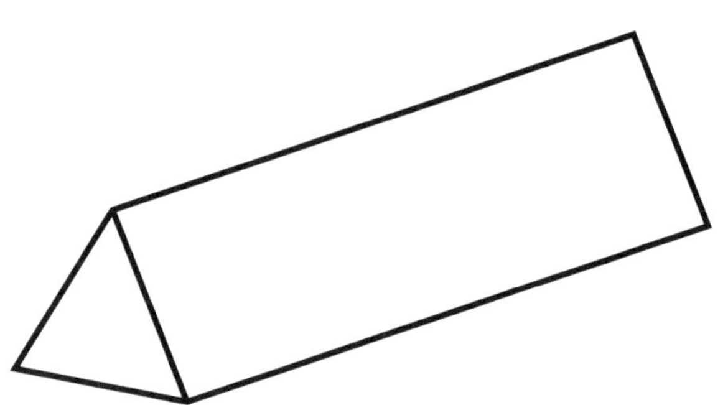

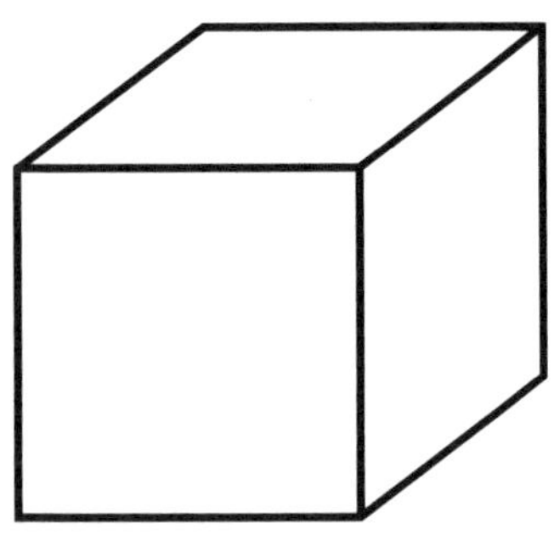

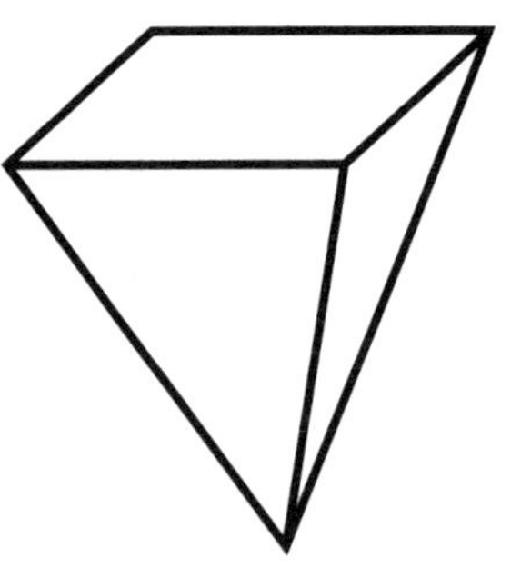

Describe the faces of each shape.

PS

Year 2 • PCM 78

Name ....

Adding 5

35p + 5p = [ ] p

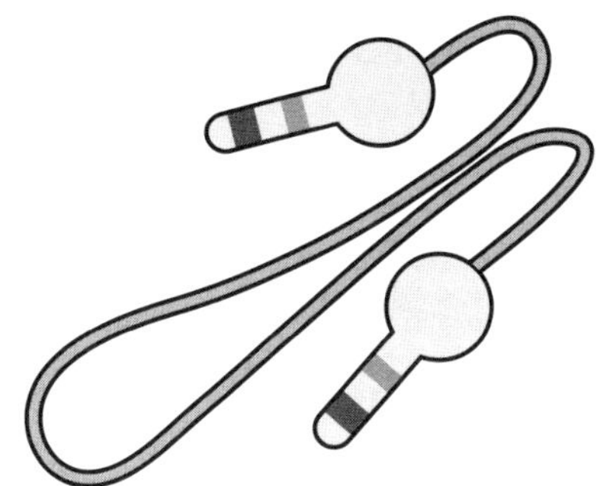

26p + 5p = [ ] p

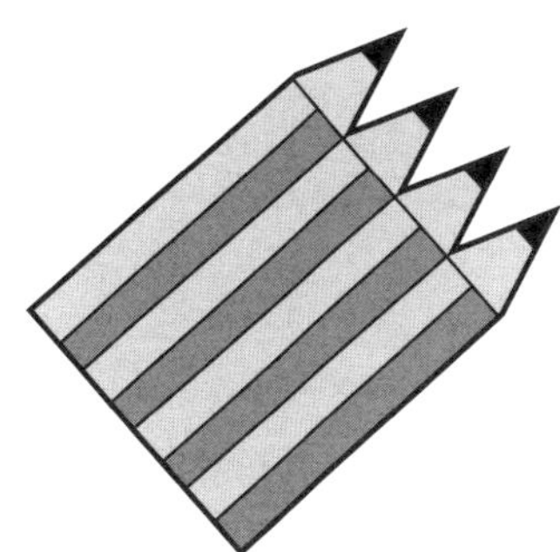

17p + 5p = [ ] p

29p + 5p = [ ] p

37p + 5p = [ ] p

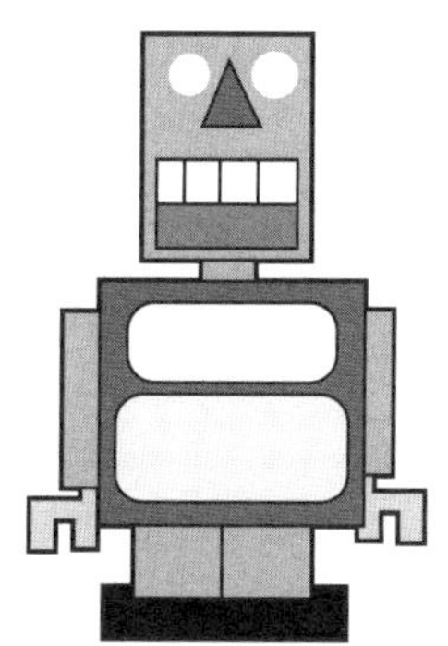

46p + 5p = [ ] p

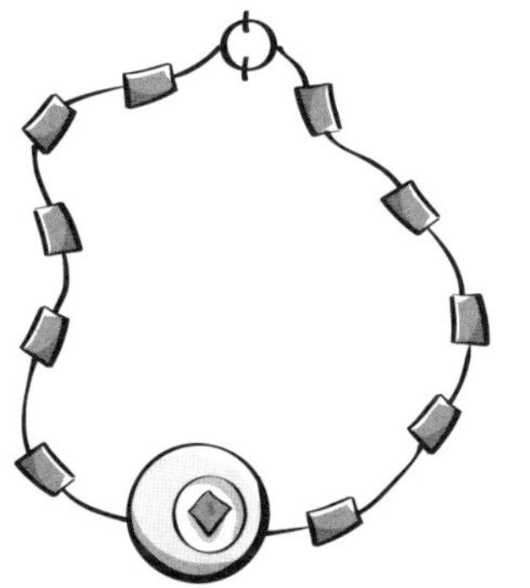

16p + 5p = [ ] p

28p + 5p = [ ] p

45p + 5p = [ ] p

Each item goes up by 5p. Write the new prices.

PS

Name ....

Differences

15 16 17 18 19 20 21

difference = 

d =

35 36 37 38 39 40 41 42 43 44 45 46

d =

57 58 59 60 61 62 63 64 65 66 67 68

d =

60 61 62 63 64 65 66 67 68 69 70 71

d =

d =

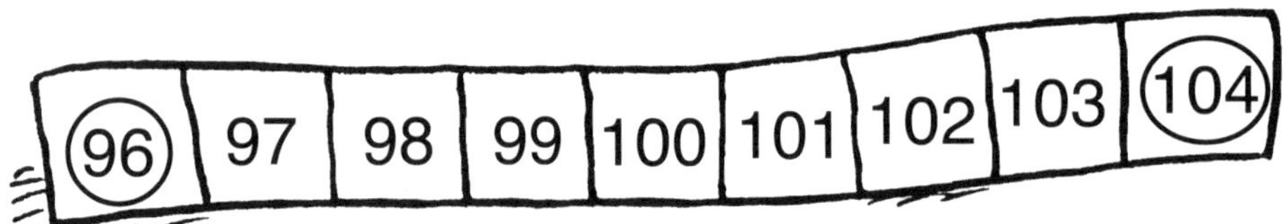

d =

69 70 71 72 73 74 75 76 77 78 79 80

d =

Write the difference between each pair of ringed numbers.

PS

Name ....

Facts to 10

$7 + \square = 10$

$10 - 1 = \square$

$\square + 5 = 10$

$10 - 3 = \square$

$8 + \square = 10$

$\square + 6 = 10$

$10 - \square = 8$

$10 - 5 = \square$

$\square + 1 = 10$

$10 - 4 = \square$

$10 - \square = 2$

$2 + \square = 10$

$\square + 3 = 10$

$10 - 7 = \square$

Write the missing numbers.

PS

Name ....

1	2	3	4	5	6	7	8	9	10
11	12	13	14	15	16	17	18	19	20
21	22	23	24	25	26	27	28	29	30
31	32	33	34	35	36	37	38	39	40
41	42	43	44	45	46	47	48	49	50
51	52	53	54	55	56	57	58	59	60
61	62	63	64	65	66	67	68	69	70
71	72	73	74	75	76	77	78	79	80
81	82	83	84	85	86	87	88	89	90
91	92	93	94	95	96	97	98	99	100

Name ....

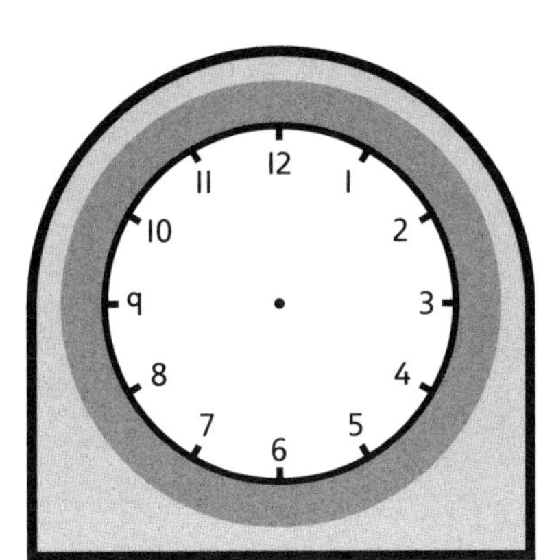
12
1
2
3
4
5
6
7
8
9
10
11

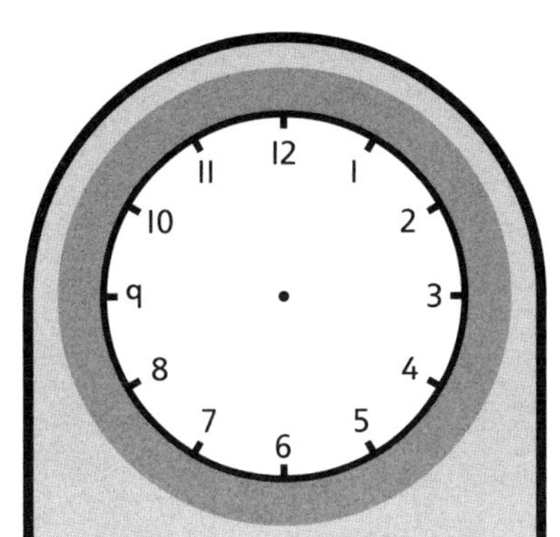
12
1
2
3
4
5
6
7
8
9
10
11

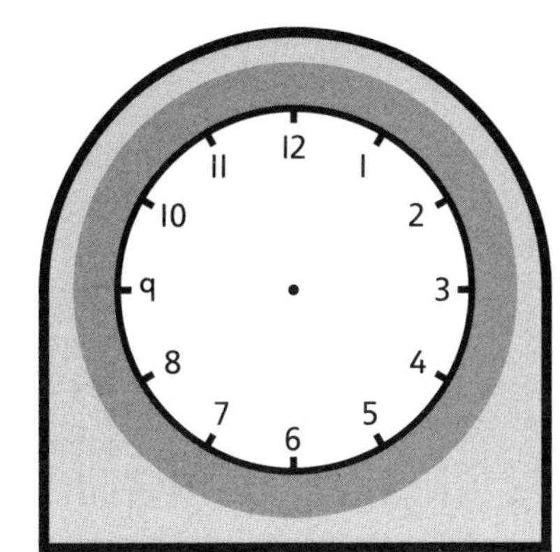
12
1
2
3
4
5
6
7
8
9
10
11

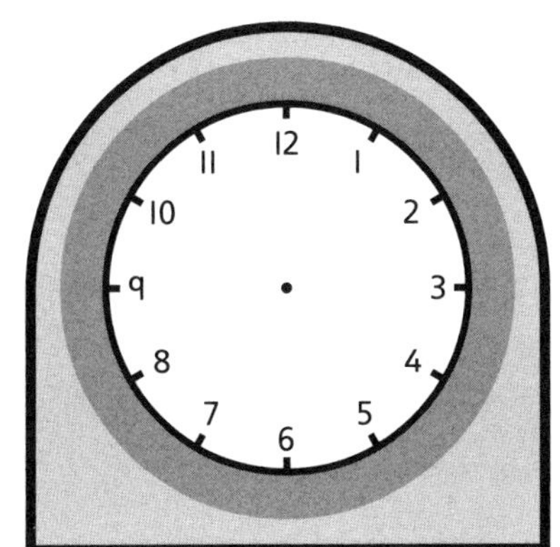
12
1
2
3
4
5
6
7
8
9
10
11

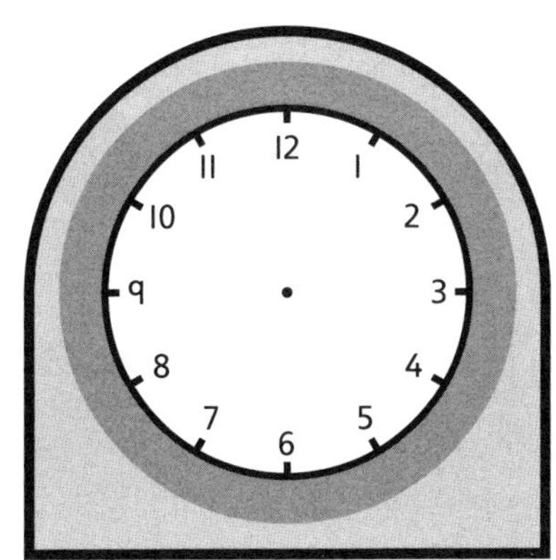
12
1
2
3
4
5
6
7
8
9
10
11

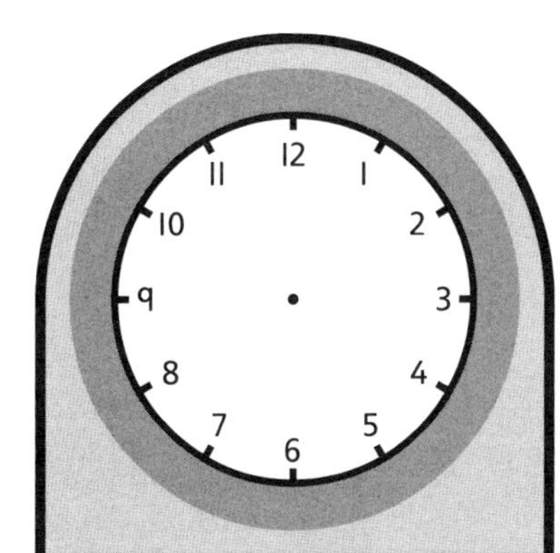
12
1
2
3
4
5
6
7
8
9
10
11

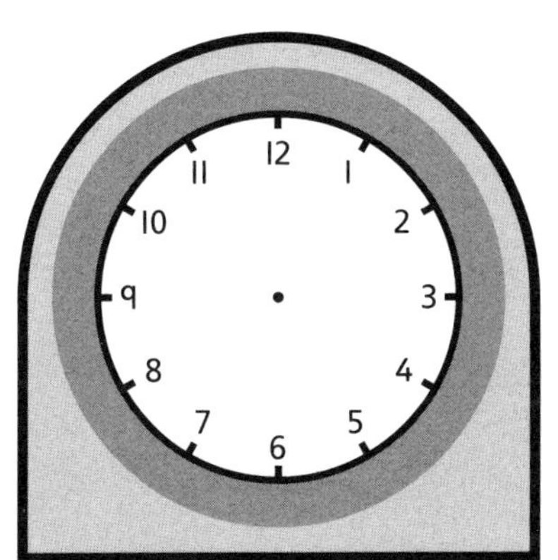
12
1
2
3
4
5
6
7
8
9
10
11

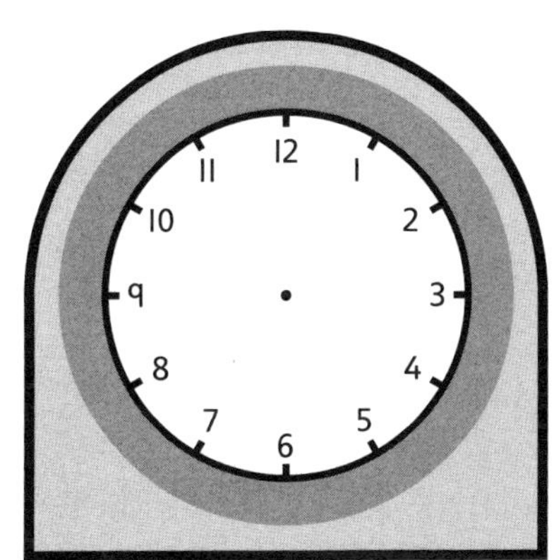
12
1
2
3
4
5
6
7
8
9
10
11

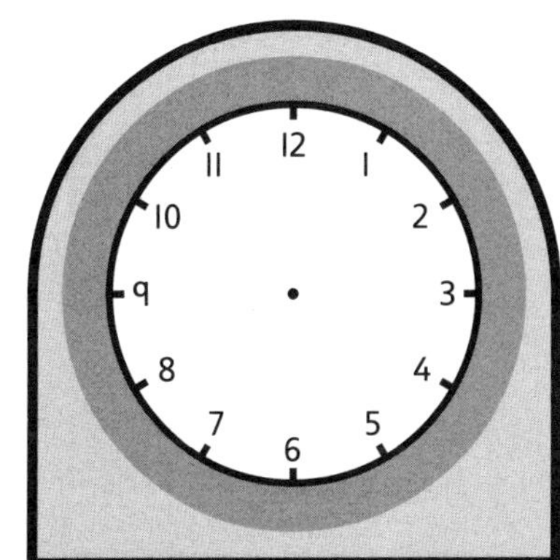
12
1
2
3
4
5
6
7
8
9
10
11

Year 2 Task Coverage Chart – matches Assessment Tasks to APP Assessment Foci

'+' indicates that content or assessment of children within the task *might* suggest evidence for a higher level.

AF/ Level	Using and applying			Number						Shape, space and measures			Handling data	
	Problem solving	Communi-cating	Reasoning	Numbers and number system	Fractions	Operations, relationships	Mental methods	Solving numerical problems	Written methods	Properties of shape	Properties of position and movement	Measures	Processing and representing data	Interpreting data
L2	**2** (A1b) **4** (B1a,b) **7** (C1a) **15** (C2a)	**4** (B1a,b) **5** (B1b) **14** (B2c,d) **16** (C2c) **17** (D2b) **18** (D2c,d)	**6** (B1c,d) **8** (D1a; B3a) **11** (E1c,d) **12** (A2d)+	**1** (A1a) **2** (A1b) **3** (A1c)+ **12** (A2d)+ **20** (A3a)+	**21** (B3b)	**10** (E1a) **23** (D3b) **25** (E3c)	**5** (B1b) **9** (D1c,d) **13** (B2a,b) **18** (D2c,d) **19** (E2c,d) **23** (D3b) **24** (E3b) **25** (E3c)	**4** (B1a,b) **6** (B1c,d) **11** (E1c,d) **16** (C2c) **19** (E2c,d)	**6** (B1c,d) **9** (D1c,d) **11** (E1c,d) **23** (D3b)	**8** (D1a; B3a) **17** (D2b)	**14** (B2c,d)	**7** (C1a) **15** (C2a) **22** (C3a)		**16** (C2c)

Test Coverage Chart

This chart shows the range of sub-levels covered by each End-of-term Test.

	1c	1b	1a	2c	2b	2a	3c	3b	3a	4c	4b	4a	5
Y1 Summer A													
Y1 Summer B													
Y2 Autumn A													
Y2 Autumn B													
Y2 Spring A													
Y2 Spring B													
Y2 Summer A													
Y2 Summer B													
Y3 Autumn A													
Y3 Autumn B													
Y3 Spring A													
Y3 Spring B													
Y3 Summer A													
Y3 Summer B													
Y4 Autumn A													
Y4 Autumn B													
Y4 Spring A													
Y4 Spring B													
Y4 Summer A													
Y4 Summer B													
Y5 Autumn A													
Y5 Autumn B													
Y5 Spring A													
Y5 Spring B													
Y5 Summer A													
Y5 Summer B													
Y6 Autumn A													
Y6 Autumn B													
Y6 Spring A													
Y6 Spring B													
Y6 Summer A													
Y6 Summer B